Machine Translation

An Introductory Guide

D. Arnold
L. Balkan
R. Lee Humphreys
S. Meijer
L. Sadler

NCC Blackwell

MANCHESTER • OXFORD

First published 1994

First published in USA 1994

NCC Blackwell Ltd.
108 Cowley Road
Oxford OX4 1JF
UK

Blackwell Publishers
238 Main Street
Cambridge, Massachusetts 02142
USA

British Library Cataloguing in Publication Data
Meijer, S.
  Machine Translation: Introductory Guide
  I. Title
  418
  ISBN 1-85554-246-3 (Hbk)
        1-85554-217-X (Pbk)

Printed in Great Britain by
T.J. Press (Padstow) Ltd, Padstow, Cornwall

This book is printed on acid-free paper.

Preface

Automatic translation between human languages ('Machine Translation') is a Science Fiction staple, and a long-term scientific dream of enormous social, political, and scientific importance. It was one of the earliest applications suggested for digital computers, but turning this dream into reality has turned out to be a much harder, and in many ways a much more interesting task than at first appeared. Nevertheless, though there remain many outstanding problems, some degree of automatic translation is now a daily reality, and it is likely that during the next decade the bulk of routine technical and business translation will be done with some kind of automatic translation tool, from humble databases containing canned translations of technical terms to genuine Machine Translation Systems that can produce reasonable draft translations (provided the input observes certain restrictions on subject matter, style, and vocabulary).

Unfortunately, how this is possible or what it really means is hard to appreciate for those without the time, patience, or training to read the relevant academic research papers, which in any case do not give a very good picture of what is involved in practice. It was for this reason that we decided to try to write a book which would be genuinely introductory (in the sense of not presupposing a background in any relevant discipline), but which would look at all aspects of Machine Translation: covering questions of what it is like to use a modern Machine Translation system, through questions about how it is done, to questions of evaluating systems, and what developments can be foreseen in the near to medium future.

We would like to express our thanks to various people. First, we would like to thank each other. The process of writing this book has been slower than we originally hoped (five authors is five pairs of hands, but also five sets of opinions). However, we think that our extensive discussions and revisions have in the end produced a better book in terms of content, style, presentation, and so on. We think we deserve no little credit for maintaining a pleasant working atmosphere while expending this level of effort and commitment while under pressure caused by other academic responsibilities.

We would also like to thank our colleagues at the Computational Linguistics and Machine Translation (CL/MT) group at the University of Essex for suggestions and practical support, especially Lisa Hamilton, Kerry Maxwell, Dave Moffat, Tim Nicholas, Melissa Parker, Martin Rondell and Andy Way.

For proofreading and constructive criticism we would like to thank John Roberts of the Department of Language and Linguistics at the University of Essex, and John Roberts and Karen Woods of NCC Blackwell. We are also grateful to those people who have helped us by checking the examples which are in languages other than English and Dutch, especially Laurence Danlos (French), and Nicola Jörn (German).

Of course, none of them is responsible for the errors of content, style or presentation that remain.

D.J. Arnold
L. Balkan
R. Lee Humphreys
S. Meijer
L. Sadler

Colchester, August 1993.

Contents

Chapter 1

Introduction and Overview

1.1 Introduction

The topic of the book is the art or science of **Automatic Translation**, or **Machine Translation** (MT) as it is generally known — the attempt to automate all, or part of the process of translating from one human language to another. The aim of the book is to introduce this topic to the general reader — anyone interested in human language, translation, or computers. The idea is to give the reader a clear basic understanding of the state of the art, both in terms of *what* is currently possible, and *how* it is achieved, and of what developments are on the horizon. This should be especially interesting to anyone who is associated with what are sometimes called "the language industries"; particularly translators, those training to be translators, and those who commission or use translations extensively. But the topics the book deals with are of general and lasting interest, as we hope the book will demonstrate, and no specialist knowledge is presupposed — no background in Computer Science, Artificial Intelligence (AI), Linguistics, or Translation Studies.

Though the purpose of this book is introductory, it is not *just* introductory. For one thing, we will, in Chapter 10, bring the reader up to date with the most recent developments. For another, as well as giving an accurate picture of the state of the art, both practically and theoretically, we have taken a position on some of what seem to us to be the key issues in MT today — the fact is that we have some axes to grind.

From the earliest days, MT has been bedevilled by grandiose claims and exaggerated expectations. MT researchers and developers should stop over-selling. The general public should stop over-expecting. One of the main aims of this book is that the reader comes to appreciate where we are today in terms of actual achievement, reasonable expectation, and unreasonable hype. This is not the kind of thing that one can sum up in a catchy headline ("No Prospect for MT" or "MT Removes the Language Barrier"), but it is something one can absorb, and which one can thereafter use to distill the essence of truth that will lie behind reports of products and research.

With all this in mind, we begin (after some introductory remarks in this chapter) with a description of what it might be like to work with a hypothetical state of the art MT system. This should allow the reader to get an overall picture of what is involved, and a realistic notion of what is actually possible. The context we have chosen for this description is that of a large organization where relatively sophisticated tools are used in the preparation of documents, and where translation is integrated into document preparation. This is partly because we think this context shows MT at its most useful. In any case, the reader unfamiliar with this situation should have no trouble understanding what is involved.

The aim of the following chapters is to 'lift the lid' on the core component of an MT system to give an idea of what goes on inside — or rather, since there are several different basic designs for MT system — to give an idea of what the main approaches are, and to point out their strengths and weaknesses.

Unfortunately, even a basic understanding of what goes on inside an MT system requires a grasp of some relatively simple ideas and terminology, mainly from Linguistics and Computational Linguistics, and this has to be given 'up front'. This is the purpose of Chapter 3. In this chapter, we describe some fundamental ideas about how the most basic sort of knowledge that is required for translation can be represented in, and used by, a computer.

In Chapter 4 we look at how the main kinds of MT system actually translate, by describing the operation of the 'Translation Engine'. We begin by describing the simplest design, which we call the **transformer** architecture. Though now somewhat old hat as regards the research community, this is still the design used in most commercial MT systems. In the second part of the chapter, we describe approaches which involve more extensive and sophisticated kinds of linguistic knowledge. We call these **Linguistic Knowledge** (LK) systems. They include the two approaches that have dominated MT research over most of the past twenty years. The first is the so-called **interlingual** approach, where translation proceeds in two stages, by analyzing input sentences into some abstract and ideally language independent meaning representation, from which translations in several different languages can potentially be produced. The second is the so-called **transfer** approach, where translation proceeds in three stages, analyzing input sentences into a representation which still retains characteristics of the original, source language text. This is then input to a special component (called a transfer component) which produces a representation which has characteristics of the target (output) language, and from which a target sentence can be produced.

The still somewhat schematic picture that this provides will be amplified in the two following chapters. In Chapter 5, we focus on what is probably the single most important component in an MT system, the dictionary, and describe the sorts of issue that arise in designing, constructing, or modifying the sort of dictionary one is likely to find in an MT system.

Chapter 6 will go into more detail about some of the problems that arise in designing and building MT systems, and, where possible, describe how they are, or could be solved. This chapter will give an idea of why MT is 'hard', of the limitations of current technology. It also begins to introduce some of the open questions for MT research that are the topic of the final chapter.

Such questions are also introduced in Chapter 7. Here we return to questions of representation and processing, which we began to look at in Chapter 3, but whereas we focused previously on morphological, syntactic, and relatively superficial semantic issues, in this chapter we turn to more abstract, 'deeper' representations — representations of various kinds of representation of meaning.

One of the features of the scenario we imagine in Chapter 2 is that texts are mainly created, stored, and manipulated electronically (for example, by word processors). In Chapter 8 we look in more detail at what this involves (or ideally would involve), and how it can be exploited to yield further benefits from MT. In particular, we will describe how standardization of electronic document formats and the general notion of standardized **markup** (which separates the content of a document from details of its realization, so that a writer, for example, specifies that a word is to be emphasised, but need not specify which typeface must be used for this) can be exploited when one is dealing with documents and their translations. This will go beyond what some readers will immediately need to know. However, we consider its inclusion important since the integration of MT into the document processing environment is an important step towards the successful use of MT. In this chapter we will also look at the benefits and practicalities of using **controlled languages** — specially simplified versions of, for example, English, and **sublanguages** — specialized languages of sub-domains. Although these notions are not central to a proper understanding of the principles of MT, they are widely thought to be critical for the successful application of MT in practice.

Continuing the orientation towards matters of more practical than theoretical importance, Chapter 9 addresses the issue of the **evaluation** of MT systems — of how to tell if an MT system is 'good'. We will go into some detail about this, partly because it is such an obvious and important question to ask, and partly because there is no other accessible discussion of the standard methods for evaluating MT systems that an interested reader can refer to.

By this time, the reader should have a reasonably good idea of what the 'state of the art' of MT is. The aim of the final chapter (Chapter 10) is to try to give the reader an idea of what the future holds by describing where MT research is going and what are currently thought to be the most promising lines of research.

Throughout the book, the reader may encounter terms and concepts with which she is unfamiliar. If necessary the reader can refer to the Glossary at the back of the book, where such terms are defined.

1.2   Why MT Matters

The topic of MT is one that we have found sufficiently interesting to spend most of our professional lives investigating, and we hope the reader will come to share, or at least understand, this interest. But whatever one may think about its intrinsic interest, it is undoubtedly an important topic — socially, politically, commercially, scientifically, and intellectually or philosophically — and one whose importance is likely to increase as the 20th Century ends, and the 21st begins.

The *social* or *political* importance of MT arises from the socio-political importance of translation in communities where more than one language is generally spoken. Here the only viable alternative to rather widespread use of translation is the adoption of a single common 'lingua franca', which (despite what one might first think) is not a particularly attractive alternative, because it involves the dominance of the chosen language, to the disadvantage of speakers of the other languages, and raises the prospect of the other languages becoming second-class, and ultimately disappearing. Since the loss of a language often involves the disappearance of a distinctive culture, and a way of thinking, this is a loss that should matter to everyone. So translation is necessary for communication — for ordinary human interaction, and for gathering the information one needs to play a full part in society. Being allowed to express yourself in your own language, and to receive information that directly affects you in the same medium, seems to be an important, if often violated, right. And it is one that depends on the availability of translation. The problem is that the demand for translation in the modern world far outstrips any possible supply. Part of the problem is that there are too few human translators, and that there is a limit on how far their productivity can be increased without automation. In short, it seems as though automation of translation is a social and political necessity for modern societies which do not wish to impose a common language on their members.

This is a point that is often missed by people who live in communities where one language is dominant, and who speak the dominant language. Speakers of English in places like Britain, and the Northern USA are examples. However, even they rapidly come to appreciate it when they visit an area where English is not dominant (for example, Welsh speaking areas of Britain, parts of the USA where the majority language is Spanish, not to mention most other countries in the world). For countries like Canada and Switzerland, and organizations like the European Community and the UN, for whom multilingualism is both a basic principle and a fact of every day life, the point is obvious.

The *commercial* importance of MT is a result of related factors. First, translation itself is commercially important: faced with a choice between a product with an instruction manual in English, and one whose manual is written in Japanese, most

English speakers will buy the former — and in the case of a repair manual for a piece of manufacturing machinery or the manual for a safety critical system, this is not just a matter of taste. Secondly, translation is expensive. Translation is a highly skilled job, requiring much more than mere knowledge of a number of languages, and in some countries at least, translators' salaries are comparable to other highly trained professionals. Moreover, delays in translation are costly. Estimates vary, but producing high quality translations of difficult material, a professional translator may average no more than about 4-6 pages of translation (perhaps 2000 words) per day, and it is quite easy for delays in translating product documentation to erode the market lead time of a new product. It has been estimated that some 40-45% of the running costs of European Community institutions are 'language costs', of which translation and interpreting are the main element. This would give a cost of something like £300 million per annum. This figure relates to translations actually done, and is a tiny fraction of the cost that would be involved in doing all the translations that could, or should be done.[1]

Scientifically, MT is interesting, because it is an obvious application and testing ground for many ideas in Computer Science, Artificial Intelligence, and Linguistics, and some of the most important developments in these fields have begun in MT. To illustrate this: the origins of Prolog, the first widely available logic programming language, which formed a key part of the Japanese 'Fifth Generation' programme of research in the late 1980s, can be found in the 'Q-Systems' language, originally developed for MT.

Philosophically, MT is interesting, because it represents an attempt to automate an activity that can require the full range of human knowledge — that is, for any piece of human knowledge, it is possible to think of a context where the knowledge is required. For example, getting the correct translation of *negatively charged electrons and protons* into French depends on knowing that protons are positively charged, so the interpretation cannot be something like "negatively charged electrons and negatively charged protons". In this sense, the extent to which one can automate translation is an indication of the extent to which one can automate 'thinking'.

Despite this, very few people, even those who are involved in producing or commissioning translations, have much idea of what is involved in MT today, either at the practical level of what it means to have and use an MT system, or at the level of what is technically feasible, and what is science fiction. In the whole of the UK there are perhaps five companies who use MT for making commercial translations on a day-to-day basis. In continental Europe, where the need for commercial translation is for historical reasons greater, the number is larger, but it still represents an extremely small proportion of the overall translation effort that is actually undertaken. In Japan, where there is an enormous need for translation of Japanese into English, MT is just beginning to become established on a commercial scale, and some familiarity with MT is becoming a standard part of the training of a professional translator.

---

[1] These estimates of CEC translation costs are from [Patterson, 1982].

Of course, theorists, developers, and sellers of MT systems must be mainly responsible for this level of ignorance and lack of uptake, and we hope this book will help here — one motivation for writing this book was our belief that an understanding of MT is an essential part of the equipment of a professional translator, and the knowledge that no other book provided this in accessible form.

We are reminded of this scale of ignorance every time we admit to working in the field of MT. After initial explanations of what MT is, the typical reaction is one of two contradictory responses (sometimes one gets both together). One is "But that's impossible — no machine could ever translate Shakespeare." The other is "Yes, I saw one of those in the Duty Free Shop when I went on holiday last summer." These reactions are based on a number of misconceptions that are worth exposing. We will look at these, as well as some correct conceptions, in the next section.

1.3   Popular Conceptions and Misconceptions

Some popular misconceptions about MT are listed on page 7. We will discuss them in turn.

• "MT is a waste of time because you will never make a machine that can translate Shakespeare".

The criticism that MT systems cannot, and will never, produce translations of great literature of any great merit is probably correct, but quite beside the point. It certainly does not show that MT is impossible. First, translating literature requires special literary skill — it is not the kind of thing that the average professional translator normally attempts. So accepting the criticism does not show that automatic translation of non-literary texts is impossible. Second, literary translation is a small proportion of the translation that has to be done, so accepting the criticism does not mean that MT is useless. Finally, one may wonder who would ever *want* to translate Shakespeare by machine — it is a job that human translators find challenging and rewarding, and it is not a job that MT systems have been designed for. The criticism that MT systems cannot translate Shakespeare is a bit like criticism of industrial robots for not being able to dance Swan Lake.

• "There was/is an MT system which translated *The spirit is willing, but the flesh is weak* into the Russian equivalent of *The vodka is good, but the steak is lousy*, and *hydraulic ram* into the French equivalent of *water goat*. MT is useless."

The 'spirit is willing' story is amusing, and it really is a pity that it is not true. However, like most MT 'howlers' it is a fabrication. In fact, for the most part, they were in circulation long before any MT system could have produced them (variants of the 'spirit is willing' example can be found in the American press as early as 1956, but sadly, there does not seem to have been an MT system in America which could translate from English into Russian until much more recently — for sound strategic reasons, work in the USA had concentrated on the translation of Russian into English, not the other way round). Of course, there are real MT howlers. Two of the nicest are the translation of French *avocat* ('advocate', 'lawyer' or 'barrister') as *avocado*, and the translation of *Les soldats sont dans le café* as *The soldiers are in the coffee*. However, they are not as easy to find as the reader might think, and they certainly do not show that MT is useless.

Some Popular Misconceptions about MT

- **False:** MT is a waste of time because you will never make a machine that can translate Shakespeare.

- **False:** There was/is an MT system which translated *The spirit is willing, but the flesh is weak* into the Russian equivalent of *The vodka is good, but the steak is lousy*, and *hydraulic ram* into the French equivalent of *water goat*. MT is useless.

- **False:** Generally, the quality of translation you can get from an MT system is very low. This makes them useless in practice.

- **False:** MT threatens the jobs of translators.

- **False:** The Japanese have developed a system that you can talk to on the phone. It translates what you say into Japanese, and translates the other speaker's replies into English.

- **False:** There is an amazing South American Indian language with a structure of such logical perfection that it solves the problem of designing MT systems.

- **False:** MT systems are machines, and buying an MT system should be very much like buying a car.

- "Generally, the quality of translation you can get from an MT system is very low. This makes them useless in practice."

Far from being useless, there are several MT systems in day-to-day use around the world. Examples include METEO (in daily since 1977 use at the Canadian Meteorological Center in Dorval, Montreal), SYSTRAN (in use at the CEC, and elsewhere), LOGOS, ALPS, ENGSPAN (and SPANAM), METAL, GLOBALINK. It is true that the number of organizations that use MT on a daily basis is relatively small, but those that do use it benefit considerably. For example, as of 1990, METEO was regularly translating around 45 000 words of weather bulletins every day, from English into French for transmission to press, radio, and television. In the 1980s, the diesel engine manufacturers Perkins Engines was saving around £4 000 on each diesel engine manual translated (using a PC version of WEIDNER system). Moreover, overall translation time per manual was more than halved from around 26 weeks to 9-12 weeks — this time saving can be very significant commercially, because a product like an engine cannot easily be marketed without user manuals.

Of course, it is true that the quality of many MT systems is low, and probably no existing system can produce really perfect translations.[2] However, this does not make MT useless. First, not every translation has to be perfect. Imagine you have in front of you a Chinese newspaper which you suspect may contain some information of crucial importance to you or your company. Even a very rough translation would help you. Apart from anything else, you would be able to work out which, if any, parts of the paper would be worth getting translated properly. Second, a human translator normally does not immediately produce a perfect translation. It is normal to divide the job of translating a document into two stages. The first stage is to produce a draft translation, i.e. a piece of running text in the target language, which has the most obvious translation problems solved (e.g. choice of terminology, etc.), but which is not necessarily perfect. This is then revised — either by the same translator, or in some large organizations by another translator — with a view to producing something that is up to standard for the job in hand. This might involve no more than checking, or it might involve quite radical revision aimed at producing something that reads as though written originally in the target language. For the most part, the aim of MT is only to automate the first, draft translation process.[3]

- "MT threatens the jobs of translators."

The quality of translation that is currently possible with MT is one reason why it is wrong to think of MT systems as dehumanizing monsters which will eliminate human translators, or enslave them. It will not eliminate them, simply because the volume of translation to be performed is so huge, and constantly growing, and because of the limitations of current and forseeable MT systems. While not an immediate prospect, it could, of course, turn out that MT enslaves human translators, by controlling the translation process, and forcing them to work on the problems it throws up, at its speed. There are no doubt examples of this happening to other professions. However, there are not many such examples, and it is not likely to happen with MT. What is more likely is that the process of producing draft translations, along with the often tedious business of looking up unknown words in dictionaries, and ensuring terminological consistency, will become automated, leaving human translators free to spend time on increasing clarity and improving style, and to translate more important and interesting documents — editorials rather than

---

[2]In fact, one can get perfect translations from one kind of system, but at the cost of radically restricting what an author can say, so one should perhaps think of such systems as (multilingual) text creation aids, rather than MT systems. The basic idea is similar to that of a phrase book, which provides the user with a collection of 'canned' phrases to use. This is fine, provided the canned text contains what the user wants to say. Fortunately, there are some situations where this is the case.

[3]Of course, the sorts of errors one finds in draft translations produced by a human translator will be rather different from those that one finds in translations produced by machine.

weather reports, for example. This idea borne out in practice: the job satisfaction of the human translators in the Canadian Meteorological Centerimproved when METEO was installed, and their job became one of checking and trying to find ways to improve the system output, rather than translating the weather bulletins by hand (the concrete effect of this was a greatly reduced turnover in translation staff at the Center).

• "The Japanese have developed a system that you can talk to on the phone. It translates what you say into Japanese, and translates the other speaker's replies into English."

The claim that the Japanese have a speech to speech translation system, of the kind described above, is pure science fiction. It is true that speech-to-speech translation is a topic of current research, and there are laboratory prototypes that can deal with a very restricted range of questions. But this research is mainly aimed at investigating how the various technologies involved in speech and language processing can be integrated, and is limited to very restricted domains (hotel bookings, for example), and messages (offering little more than a phrase book in these domains). It will be several years before even this sort of system will be in any sort of real use. This is partly because of the limitations of speech systems, which are currently fine for recognizing isolated words, uttered by a single speaker, for which the system has been specially trained, in quiet conditions, but which do not go far beyond this. However, it is also because of the limitations of the MT system (see later chapters).

• "There is an amazing South American Indian language with a structure of such logical perfection that it solves the problem of designing MT systems."

The South American Indian language story is among the most irritating for MT researchers. First, the point about having a 'perfectly logical structure' is almost certainly completely false. Such perfection is mainly in the eye of the beholder — Diderot was convinced that the word order of French exactly reflected the order of thought, a suggestion that non-French speakers do not find very convincing. What people generally mean by this is that a language is very simple to describe. Now, as far as anyone can tell all human languages are pretty much as complicated as each other. It's hard to be definite, since the idea of simplicity is difficult to pin down, but the general impression is that if a language has a very simple syntax, for example, it will compensate by having a more complicated morphology (word structure), or phonology (sound structure).[4] However, even if one had a very neat logical language, it is hard to see that this would solve the MT problem, since one would still have to perform automatic translation into, and out of, this language.

• "MT systems are machines, and buying an MT system should be very much like

---

[4]Of course, some languages have larger vocabularies than others, but this is mainly a matter of how many things the language is used to talk about (not surprisingly, the vocabulary which Shakespeare's contemporaries had for discussing high-energy physics was rather impoverished), but all languages have ways of forming new words, and this has nothing to do with logical perfection.

buying a car."

There are really two parts to this misconception. The first relates to the sense in which MT systems are machines. They are, of course, but only in the sense that modern word processors are machines. It is more accurate to think of MT systems as *programs* that run on computers (which really are machines). Thus, when one talks about buying, modifying, or repairing an MT system, one is talking about buying, modifying or repairing a piece of *software*. It was not always so — the earliest MT systems were dedicated machines, and even very recently, there were some MT vendors who tried to sell their systems with specific hardware, but this is becoming a thing of the past. Recent systems can be installed on different types of computers. The second part of the misconception is the idea that one would take an MT system and 'drive it away', as one would a car. In fact, this is unlikely to be possible, and a better analogy is with buying a house — what one buys may be immediately habitable, but there is a considerable amount of work involved in adapting it to one's own special needs. In the case of a house this might involve changes to the decor and plumbing. In the case of an MT system this will involve additions to the dictionaries to deal with the vocabulary of the subject area and possibly the type of text to be translated. There will also be some work involved in integrating the system into the rest of one's document processing environment. More of this in Chapters 2 and 8. The importance of customization, and the fact that changes to the dictionary form a major part of the process is one reason why we have given a whole chapter to discussion of the dictionary (Chapter 5).

Against these misconceptions, we should place the genuine facts about MT. These are listed on page 11.

The correct conclusion is that MT, although imperfect, is not only a possibility, but an actuality. But it is important to see the product in a proper perspective, to be aware of its strong points and shortcomings.

Machine Translation started out with the hope and expectation that most of the work of translation could be handled by a system which contained all the information we find in a standard paper bilingual dictionary. Source language words would be replaced with their target language translational equivalents, as determined by the built-in dictionary, and where necessary the order of the words in the input sentences would be rearranged by special rules into something more characteristic of the target language. In effect, correct translations suitable for immediate use would be manufactured in two simple steps. This corresponds to the view that translation is nothing more than word substitution (determined by the dictionary) and reordering (determined by reordering rules).

Reason and experience show that 'good' MT cannot be produced by such delightfully simple means. As all translators know, word for word translation doesn't produce a satisfying target language text, not even when some local reordering rules (e.g. for the position of the adjective with regard to the noun which it modifies) have been

Some Facts about MT

- **True:** MT is useful. The METEO system has been in daily use since 1977. As of 1990, it was regularly translating around 45 000 words daily. In the 1980s, The diesel engine manufacturers Perkins Engines was saving around £4000 and up to 15 weeks on each manual translated.

- **True:** While MT systems sometimes produce howlers, there are many situations where the ability of MT systems to produce reliable, if less than perfect, translations at high speed is valuable.

- **True:** In some circumstances, MT systems can produce good quality output: less than 4% of METEO output requires any correction by human translators at all (and most of these are due to transmission errors in the original texts). Even where the quality is lower, it is often easier and cheaper to revise 'draft quality' MT output than to translate entirely by hand.

- **True:** MT does not threaten translators' jobs. The need for translation is vast and unlikely to diminish, and the limitations of current MT systems are too great. However, MT systems can take over some of the boring, repetitive translation jobs and allow human translation to concentrate on more interesting tasks, where their specialist skills are really needed.

- **True:** Speech-to-Speech MT is still a research topic. In general, there are many open research problems to be solved before MT systems will be come close to the abilities of human translators.

- **True:** Not only are there are many open research problems in MT, but building an MT system is an arduous and time consuming job, involving the construction of grammars and very large monolingual and bilingual dictionaries. There is no 'magic solution' to this.

- **True:** In practice, before an MT system becomes really useful, a user will typically have to invest a considerable amount of effort in customizing it.

included in the system. Translating a text requires not only a good knowledge of the vocabulary of both source and target language, but also of their grammar — the system of rules which specifies which sentences are well-formed in a particular language and which are not. Additionally it requires some element of **real world knowledge** — knowledge of the nature of things out in the world and how they work together — and technical knowledge of the text's subject area. Researchers certainly believe that much can be done to satisfy these requirements, but producing systems which actually do so is far from easy. Most effort in the past 10 years or so has gone into increasing the subtlety, breadth and depth of the linguistic or grammatical knowledge available to systems. We shall take a more detailed look at these developments in due course.

In growing into some sort of maturity, the MT world has also come to realize that the 'text in → translation out' assumption — the assumption that MT is solely a matter of switching on the machine and watching a faultless translation come flying out — was rather too naive. A translation process starts with providing the MT system with *usable* input. It is quite common that texts which are submitted for translation need to be adapted (for example, typographically, or in terms of format) before the system can deal with them. And when a text can actually be submitted to an MT system, and the system produces a translation, the output is almost invariably deemed to be grammatically and translationally imperfect. Despite the increased complexity of MT systems they will never — within the forseeable future — be able to handle all types of text reliably and accurately. This normally means that the translation will have to be corrected (post-edited) and usually the person best equipped to do this is a translator.

This means that MT will only be profitable in environments that can exploit the strong points to the full. As a consequence, we see that the main impact of MT in the immediate future will be in large corporate environments where substantial amounts of translation are performed. The implication of this is that MT is not (yet) for the individual self-employed translator working from home, or the untrained lay-person who has the occasional letter to write in French. This is not a matter of cost: MT systems sell at anywhere between a few hundred pounds and over £100 000. It is a matter of effective use. The aim of MT is to achieve faster, and thus cheaper, translation. The lay-person or self-employed translator would probably have to spend so much time on dictionary updating and/or post-editing that MT would not be worthwhile. There is also the problem of getting input texts in machine readable form, otherwise the effort of typing will outweigh any gains of automation. The real gains come from integrating the MT system into the whole document processing environment (see Chapter 2), and they are greatest when several users can share, for example, the effort of updating dictionaries, efficiencies of avoiding unnecessary retranslation, and the benefits of terminological consistency.

Most of this book is about MT today, and to some extent tomorrow. But MT is a subject with an interesting and dramatic past, and it is well worth a brief description.

1.4   A Bit of History

There is some dispute about who first had the idea of translating automatically between human languages, but the actual development of MT can be traced to conversations and correspondence between Andrew D. Booth, a British crystallographer, and Warren Weaver of the Rockefeller Foundation in 1947, and more specifically to a memorandum written by Weaver in 1949 to the Rockerfeller Foundation which included the following two sentences.

"I have a text in front of me which is written in Russian but I am going to pretend that it is really written in English and that it has been coded in some strange symbols. All I need to do is strip off the code in order to retrieve the information contained in the text."

The analogy of translation and decoding may strike the sophisticated reader as simplistic (however complicated coding gets it is still basically a one-for-one substitution process where there is only one right answer — translation is a far more complex and subtle business), and later in the memorandum Weaver proposed some other more sophisticated views,[5] but it had the virtue of turning an apparently difficult task into one that could be approached with the emergent computer technology (there had been considerable success in using computers in cryptography during the Second World War). This memorandum sparked a significant amount of interest and research, and by the early 1950s there was a large number of research groups working in Europe and the USA, representing a significant financial investment (equivalent to around £20 000 000). But, despite some success, and the fact that many research questions were raised that remain important to this day, there was widespread disappointment on the part of funding authorities at the return on investment that this represented, and doubts about the possibility of automating translation in general, or at least in the current state of knowledge.

The theoretical doubts were voiced most clearly by the philosopher Bar-Hillel in a 1959 report, where he argued that fully automatic, high quality, MT (FAHQMT) was impossible, not just at present, but in *principle*. The problem he raised was that of finding the right translation for *pen* in a context like the following:

(1)   Little John was looking for his toy box. Finally he found it. The box was in the pen. John was very happy.

---

[5]Weaver described an analogy of individuals in tall closed towers who communicate (badly) by shouting to each other. However, the towers have a common foundation and basement. Here communication is easy: "Thus it may be true that the way to translate ... is not to attempt the direct route, shouting from tower to tower. Perhaps the way is to descend, from each language, down to the common base of human communication — the real but as yet undiscovered universal language."

The argument was that (i) here *pen* could only have the interpretation *play-pen*, not the alternative *writing instrument* interpretation, (ii) this could be critical in deciding the correct translation for *pen*, (iii) discovering this depends on general knowledge about the world, and (iv) there could be no way of building such knowledge into a computer. Some of these points are well taken. Perhaps FAHQMT is impossible. But this does not mean that any form of MT is impossible or useless, and in Chapter 7 we will look at some of the ways one might go about solving this problem. Nevertheless, historically, this was important in suggesting that research should focus on more fundamental issues in the processing and understanding of human languages.

The doubts of funding authorities were voiced in the report which the US National Academy of Sciences commissioned in 1964 when it set up the Automatic Language Processing Advisory Committee (ALPAC) to report on the state of play with respect to MT as regards quality, cost, and prospects, as against the existing cost of, and need for translation. Its report, the so-called *ALPAC Report*, was damning, concluding that there was no shortage of human translators, and that there was no immediate prospect of MT producing useful translation of general scientific texts. This report led to the virtual end of Government funding in the USA. Worse, it led to a general loss of morale in the field, as early hopes were perceived to be groundless.

The spectre of the ALPAC report, with its threats of near complete withdrawal of funding, and demoralization, still haunts workers in MT. Probably it should not, because the achievements of MT are real, even if they fall short of the idea of FAHQMT all the time — useful MT is neither science fiction, nor merely a topic for scientific speculation. It is a daily reality in some places, and for some purposes. However, the fear is understandable, because the conclusion of the report was almost entirely mistaken. First, the idea that there was no need for machine translation is one that should strike the reader as absurd, given what we said earlier. One can only understand it in the anglo-centric context of cold-war America, where the main reason to translate was to gain intelligence about Soviet activity. Similarly, the suggestion that there was no prospect of successful MT seems to have been based on a narrow view of FAHQMT — in particular, on the idea that MT which required revision was not 'real' MT. But, keeping in mind the considerable time gain that can be achieved by automating the draft translation stage of the process, this view is naive. Moreover, there were, even at the time the report was published, three systems in regular, if not extensive, use (one at the Wright Patterson USAF base, one at the Oak Ridge Laboratory of the US Atomic Energy Commission, and one the EURATOM Centre at Ispra in Italy).

Nevertheless, the central conclusion that MT did not represent a useful goal for research or development work had taken hold, and the number of groups and individuals involved in MT research shrank dramatically. For the next ten years, MT research became the preserve of groups funded by the Mormon Church, who had an interest in bible translation (the work that was done at Brigham Young University in Provo, Utah ultimately led to the WEIDNER and ALPS systems, two notable early commercial systems), and a handful of groups in Canada (notably the TAUM group in Montreal, who developed the METEO system mentioned earlier), the USSR (notably the groups led by Mel'čuk, and Apresian), and Europe (notably the GETA group in Grenoble, probably the single most influential group of this period, and the SUSY group in Saarbrücken). A small fraction of the funding and effort that had been devoted to MT was put into more fundamental research on Computational Linguistics, and Artificial Intelligence, and some of this work took MT as a long term objective, even in the USA (Wilks' work on AI is notable in this respect). It was not until the late 1970s that MT research underwent something of a renaissance.

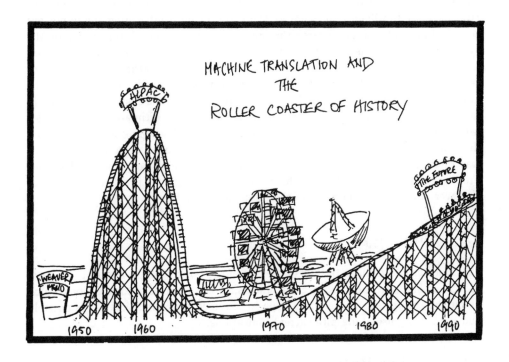

Machine Translation and the Roller Coaster of History

There were several signs of this renaissance. The Commission of the European Communities (CEC) purchased the English-French version of the SYSTRAN system, a greatly improved descendent of the earliest systems developed at Georgetown University (in Washington, DC), a Russian-English system whose development had continued throughout the lean years after ALPAC, and which had been used by both the USAF and NASA. The CEC also commissioned the development of a French-English version, and Italian-English version. At about the same time, there was a rapid expansion of MT activity in Japan, and the CEC also began to set up what was to become the EUROTRA project, building on the work of the GETA and SUSY groups. This was perhaps the largest, and certainly among the most ambitious research and development projects in Natural Language Processing. The aim was to produce a 'pre-industrial' MT system of advanced design (what we call a Linguistic Knowledge system) for the EC languages. Also in the late 1970s the Pan American Health Organization (PAHO) began development of a Spanish-English MT system (SPANAM), the United States Air Force funded work on the METAL system at the Linguistics Research Center, at the University of Texas in Austin, and the results of work at the TAUM group led to the installation of the METEO system. For the most part, the history of the 1980s in MT is the history of these initiatives, and the exploitation of results in neighbouring disciplines.

As one moves nearer to the present, views of history are less clear and more subjective. Chapter 10 will describe what we think are the most interesting and important technical innovations. As regards the practical and commercial application of MT systems. The systems that were on the market in the late 1970s have had their ups and downs, but for commercial and marketing reasons, rather than scientific or technical reasons, and a number of the research projects which were started in the 1970s and 1980s have led to working, commercially available systems. This should mean that MT is firmly established, both as an area of legitimate research, and a useful application of technology. But researching and developing MT systems is a difficult task both technically, and in terms of management, organization and infrastructure, and it is an expensive task, in terms of time, personnel, and money. From a technical point of view, there are still fundamental problems to address. However, all of this is the topic of the remainder of this book.

1.5 Summary

This chapter has given an outline of the rest of the book, and given a potted history of MT. It has also tried to lay a few ghosts, in the form of misconceptions which haunt the enterprise. Above all we hope to convince the reader that MT is possible and potentially useful, despite current limitations.

1.6 Further Reading

A broad, practically oriented view of the field of current MT by a variety of authors can be found in [Newton, 1992a]. Generally speaking, the best source of material that takes an MT user's viewpoint is the series of books titled *Translating and the Computer*, with various editors and publishers, including [Lawson, 1982a], [Snell, 1979], [Snell, 1982], [Lawson, 1982b], [Picken, 1985], [Picken, 1986], [Picken, 1987], [Picken, 1988], [Mayorcas, 1990], [Picken, 1990], and [Mayorcas, Forthcoming]. These are the published proceedings of the annual Conference on Translating and the Computer, sponsored by Aslib (The Association for Information Management), and the Institute for Translation and Interpreting.

By far the best technical introduction to MT is [Hutchins and Somers, 1992]. This would be appropriate for readers who want to know more technical and scientific details about MT, and we will often refer to it in later chapters. This book contains useful discussions of some of the main MT systems, but for descriptions of these systems by their actual designers the reader should look at [Slocum, 1988], and [King, 1987]. Slocum's introduction to the former, [Slocum, 1986], is particularly recommended as an overview of the key issues in MT. These books all contain detailed descriptions of the research of the TAUM group which developed the METEO system referred to in section 1.3. The METEO system is discussed further in Chapter 8.

A short assessment of the current state of MT in terms of availability and use of systems in Europe, North America, and Japan and East Asia can be found in [Pugh, 1992]. An up-to-date picture of the state of MT as regards both commercial and scientific points of view is provided every two years by the *Machine Translation Summits*. A report of one of these can be found in [Nagao, 1989]. There is a description of the successful use of MT in a corporate setting in [Newton, 1992b].

On the history of MT (which we have outlined here, but which will not be discussed again), the most comprehensive discussion can be found in [Hutchins, 1986], though there are also useful discussions in [Warwick, 1987], and [Buchmann, 1987]. [Nagao, 1986] also provides a useful insight into the history of MT, together with a general introduction to MT. The ALPAC report is [Pierce and Carroll, 1966]. The work of Wilks' that is referred to in section 1.4 is [Wilks, 1973].

For general descriptions and discussion of the activity of translation (both human and machine) [Picken, 1989] is a useful and up-to-date source. This contains references to (for example) works on translation theory, and gives a great deal of practical information of value to translators (such as lists national translators' and interpreters' organizations, and bibliographies of translations).

For up-to-date information about the state of MT, there is the newsletter of the International Association for Machine Translation *MT News International*. See the list of addresses on page 207.

Chapter 2

Machine Translation in Practice

2.1 Introduction

At the time of writing, the use of MT — or indeed, any sort of computerised tool for translation support — is completely unknown to the vast majority of individuals and organizations in the world, even those involved in the so called 'language industries', like translators, terminologists, technical writers, etc.

Given this, one of the first things a reader is likely to want to know about MT is what it might be like to work with an MT system and how it fits in with the day-to-day business of translation. The purpose of the present chapter is to provide just such information — a view of MT at the user level, and from the outside. In later chapters we shall in effect lift off the covers of an MT system and take a look at what goes on inside. For the moment, however, the central components of an MT system are treated as a black box.

We introduce the business of MT in terms of a scenario describing the usage of MT inside a fairly large multinational corporation. The scenario is not based exactly on any one existing corporation. Our description is somewhat idealised in that we assume methods of working which are only just starting to come into use. However, there is nothing idly futuristic in our description: it is based on a consensus view of commercial MT experts and envisages tools which we know to be either already available or in an advanced state of development in Europe or elsewhere. The commercialisation of MT is not awaiting a 'miracle breakthrough' in the science of MT; it is not necessary, nor do we expect it to occur. What will happen over the next ten years are progressive improvements in functionality and performance which, taken in conjunction with the continuously falling costs of basic computing power, will ensure that MT becomes more and more cost effective. In short, we have no doubt that in general outline, if not in every detail, we are sketching the professional life of the machine translator in the 90s, and of most translators in the early part of the next century.

2.2   The Scenario

Let us suppose that you are a native English speaker engaged as a professional German-English translator in the Language Centre for a multinational manufacturing company. One of the products this company supplies is computer products. In this organization the Language Centre is principally responsible for the translation of documents created within the company into a variety of European and Oriental languages. The Language Centre is also charged with exercising control over the content and presentation of company documentation in general. To this end, it attempts to specify standards for the final appearance of documents in distributed form, including style, terminology, and content in general. The overall policy is enshrined in the form of a corporate *Document Design and Content Guide* which the Centre periodically updates and revises.

The material for which MT is to be used consists of technical documentation such as User and Repair manuals for software and hardware products manufactured or sourced by the company. Some classes of highly routine internal business correspondence are also submitted for MT. Legal and marketing material, and much external business correspondence, is normally translated by hand, although some translators in the organization prefer to use MT here as well.

All material for translation is available in electronic form on a computer network which supports the company's documentation system. Although most documents will be printed out at some point as standard paper User Manuals and so forth, the system also supports the preparation of multi-media hypertext documents. These are documents which exist primarily in electronic form with a sophisticated cross-reference system; they contain both text and pictures (and perhaps speech and other sounds). These documents are usually distributed to their final users as CD-ROMs, although they can be distributed in other electronic forms, including electronic mail. Printed versions of these documents can also be made.

Everyone in the language department has a workstation — an individual computer. These are linked together by the network. The documentation system which runs on this network allows users to create and modify documents by typing in text; in other words, it provides very sophisticated word processing facilities. It also provides sophisticated means for storing and retrieving electronic documents, and for passing them around the network inside the company or via external networks to external organizations. As is usual with current computer systems, everything is done with the help of a friendly interface based on windows, icons and menus, selections being made with a mouse.

The MT system which you use is called ETRANS and forms part of the overall documentation system. (ETRANS is just a name we have invented for a prototypical MT system.) Parts of an electronic document on the system can be sent to the MT system in the same way that they can be sent to a printer or to another device or facility on the network. ETRANS is simultaneously available from any workstation and, for each person using it, behaves as if it is his or her own personal MT system.

Earlier this morning, one of the technical authors had completed (two days after the deadline) a User Manual for a printer the company is about to launch. The text is in German. Although this author works in a building 50 kilometres away, the network ensures that the document is fully accessible from your workstation. What follows is a fragment of the text which you are viewing in a window on the workstation screen and which you are going to translate:

German Source Text

Druckdichte Einstellung
Die gedruckte Seite sollte von exzellenter Qualität sein. Es gibt aber eine Reihe von Umweltfaktoren, wie hohe Temperatur und Feuchtigkeit, die Variationen in der Druckdichte verursachen können. Falls die Testseite zu hell oder zu dunkel aussieht, verstellen Sie die Druckdichte am Einstellknopf an der linken Seite des Druckers (Figur 2-25).
Einstellung der Druckdichte:

- Drehen Sie den Knopf ein oder zwei Positionen in Richtung des dunklen Indikators.

- Schalten Sie den Drucker für einen Moment aus und dann wieder ein, so daß die Testseite gedruckt wird.

- Wiederholen Sie die beiden vorherigen Schritte solange, bis Sie grau auf dem Blatthintergrund sehen, ähnlich wie bei leicht unsauberen Kopien eines Photokopierers.

- Drehen Sie den Knopf eine Position zurück.

Jetzt können Sie den Drucker an den Computer anschliessen.
Falls Sie den Drucker an einen Macintosh Computer anschliessen, fahren Sie mit den Instruktionen im Kapitel 3 fort. Falls Sie einen anderen Computer benutzen, fahren Sie fort mit Kapitel 4.

As with all the technical documents submitted to ETRANS, all the sentences are relatively short and rather plain. Indeed, it was written in accordance with the Language Centre document specification and with MT very much in mind. There are no obvious idioms or complicated linguistic constructions. Many or all of the technical terms relating to printers (e.g. *Druckdichte* 'print density') are in regular use in the company and are stored and defined in paper or electronic dictionaries available to the company's technical authors and translators.

To start up ETRANS, you click on the icon bearing an ETRANS logo, and this pops up a menu giving various translation options. ETRANS handles six languages: English, German, French, Italian, Spanish and Japanese. The printer document needs to be translated into English, so you select English as the target language option. Another menu shows the source language to be used. In this case, there is no need to select German because ETRANS has already had a very quick look at your printer document and decided, given rather superficial criteria such as the presence of umlauts and other characteristics of German orthography, that it is probably German text. If ETRANS had guessed wrongly — as it sometimes does — then you could select the correct source language from the menu yourself. By clicking on an additional menu of ETRANS options, you start it translating in batch or full-text mode; that is, the whole text will be translated automatically without any intervention on your part. The translation starts appearing in a separate screen window more or less immediately. However, since the full source text is quite long, it will take some time to translate it in its entirety. Rather than sit around, you decide to continue with the revision of another translation in another window. You will look at the output as soon as it has finished translating the first chapter.

The output of ETRANS can be found on page 23. The quality of this raw output is pretty much as you expect from ETRANS. Most sentences are more or less intelligible even if you don't go back to the German source. (Sometimes some sentences may be completely unintelligible.) The translation is relatively accurate in the sense that it is not misleading — it doesn't lead you to think that the source text says one thing when it really says something quite the opposite. However, the translation is very far from being a good specimen of English. For one thing, ETRANS clearly had difficulties with choosing the correct translation of the German word *ein* which has three possible English equivalents: *a/an*, *on* and *one*.

(1) a. Turn the button $\boxed{\text{an}}$ or two positions in direction of the dark indicator.

    b. Switch off the printer for a moment and then again $\boxed{\text{a}}$, so that the test page is printed.

Apart from these details, it has also made quite a mess of a whole phrase:

(2) ....., similarly like at easily unclean copies of a photocopier.

In order to post-edit such phrases it will be necessary to refer back to the German source text.

MT Output

Print density adjustment
The printed page should be from excellent quality. There is however a series of environmental factors, how high temperature and humidity, can cause the variations in the print density.
If the test page looks too light or too darkly, adjust the print density at the tuner at the left page of the printer (figure 2-25).
Adjustment of the print density:

- Turn the button an or two positions in direction of the dark indicator.

- Switch off the printer for a moment and then again a, so that the test page is printed.

- Repeat the two previous steps as long as, until you see Gray on the background of the page, similarly like at easily unclean copies of a photocopier.

- Turn back the button a position.

Now you can connect the printer to the computer.
If you connect the printer to a Macintosh computers, continue with the instructions in the chapter 3. If you use an other computer, continue with chapters 4.

Leaving ETRANS to continue translating later chapters of the document, you start post-editing the first chapter by opening up a post-edit window, which interleaves a copy of the raw ETRANS output with the corresponding source sentences (e.g. so that each source sentence appears next to its proposed translation). Your workstation screen probably now looks something like the Figure on page 24.

Icons and menus give access to large scale on-line multilingual dictionaries — either the ones used by the ETRANS itself or others specifically intended for human users. You post-edit the raw MT using the range of word-processing functions provided by the document processing system. Using search facilities, you skip through the document looking for all instances of *a*, *an* or *one*, since you know that these are often wrong and may need replacement. (Discussions are in progress with the supplier of ETRANS who has promised to look into this problem and make improvements.) After two or three other global searches for known problem areas, you start to go through the document making corrections sentence by sentence. The result of this is automatically separated from the source text, and can be displayed in yet another window. Page 25 shows what your workstation screen might now look like.

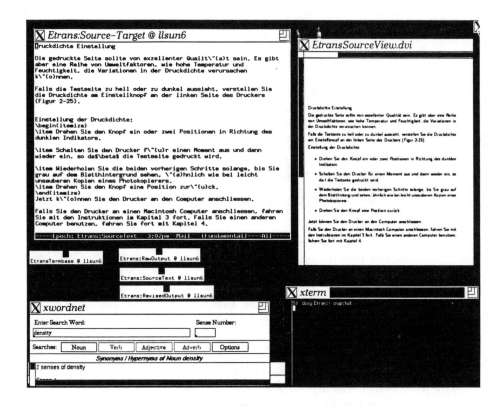

During post-editing, the source text and target text can be displayed on alternate lines, which permits easy editing of the target text. This can be seen in the window at the top left of the screen. Below this are windows and icons for on-line dictionaries and termbanks, the source text alone, and the edited target text, etc. The window on the right shows the source text as it was originally printed.

Figure 2.1 Translators' Workstation while Post-Editing a Translation

Note that ETRANS has left the document format completely unaltered. It may be that the translation is actually slightly longer (or shorter) than the source text; any necessary adjustment to the pagination of the translation compared to the source is a matter for the document processing system.

After post-editing the remaining text, you have almost completed the entire translation process. Since it is not uncommon for translators to miss some small translation errors introduced by the MT system, you observe company policy by sending your post-edited electronic text to a colleague to have it double-checked. The result is similar to that on page 26.

The only thing left to be done is to update the term dictionary, by adding any technical terms that have appeared in the document with their translation terms which other translators should in future translate in the same way, and report any new errors the MT system has committed (with a view to the system being improved in the future).

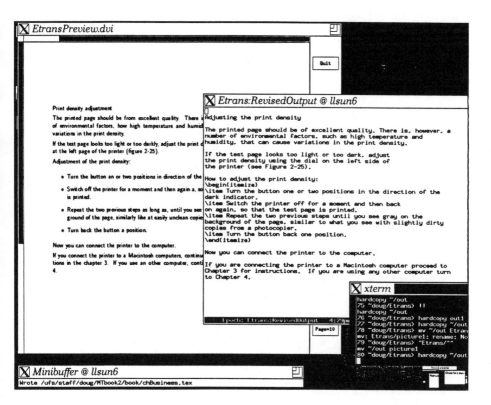

Having finished revising the translation, the result can be checked. One of the windows contains a preview of how the revised target text will look when it is printed. The other contains the revised translation, which can be edited for further corrections.

Figure 2.2 Translators' Workstation Previewing Output

So that, in outline, is how MT fits into the commercial translation process. Let us review the individuals, entities and processes involved. Proceeding logically, we have as individuals:

- Documentation managers, who specify company policy on documentation.

- Authors of texts who (ideally) write with MT in mind, following certain established guidelines.

- Translators who manage the translation system in all respects pertaining to its day to day operation and its linguistic performance.

In many cases the document management role will be fulfilled by translators or technical authors. For obvious reasons, there will be fairly few individuals who are both technical authors and translators.

Post-edited translation

Adjusting the print density
The printed page should be of excellent quality. There is, however, a number of environmental factors, such as high temperature and humidity, that can cause variations in the print density.
If the test page looks too light or too dark, adjust the print density using the dial on the left side of the printer (see Figure 2-25).
How to adjust the print density:

- Turn the button one or two positions in the direction of the dark indicator.

- Switch the printer off for a moment and then back on again, so that the test page is printed.

- Repeat the two previous steps until you see gray on the background of the page, similar to what you see with slightly dirty copies from a photocopier.

- Turn the button back one position.

Now you can connect the printer to the computer.
If you are connecting the printer to a Macintosh computer proceed to Chapter 3 for instructions. If you are using any other computer turn to Chapter 4.

The important entities in the process are:

- Multi-Lingual Electronic Documents which contain text for translation.

- The Document Preparation system which helps to create, revise, distribute and archive electronic documents.

- The Translation System which operates on source text in a document to produce a translated text of that document.

Clearly any translation system is likely to be a very complex and sophisticated piece of software; its design at the linguistic level is discussed in detail in other chapters in this book. A detailed discussion of Electronic Documents can be found in Chapter 8.

Finally, the various processes or steps in the whole business are:

- Document Preparation (which includes authoring and pre-editing).

- The Translation Process, mediated by the translation system, perhaps in conjunction with the translator.

- Document Revision (which is principally a matter of post-editing by the translator).

The scenario gave a brief flavour of all three steps. We shall now examine each of them in rather more detail.

2.3   Document Preparation: Authoring and Pre-Editing

The corporate language policy as described in the scenario tries to ensure that text which is submitted to an MT system is written in a way which helps to achieve the best possible raw MT output. A human translator will often be able to turn a badly written text into a well written translation; an MT system certainly will not. Bad input means bad output. Exactly what constitutes *good* input will vary a little from system to system. However, it is easy to identify some simple writing rules and strategies that can improve the performance of almost any general-purpose MT system. Here are some example rules:

Basic Writing Rules

- Keep sentences short.

- Make sure sentences are grammatical.

- Avoid complicated grammatical constructions.

- Avoid (so far as possible) words which have several meanings.

- In technical documents, only use technical words and terms which are well established, well defined and known to the system.

Our example rules indicate sentences should be short. This is because MT systems find it difficult to analyse long sentences quickly or — more importantly — reliably.

Lacking a human perspective, the system is always uncertain about the correct way to analyse a sentence; as the sentence gets longer, the number of uncertainties increases rather dramatically.

Sentences should also be grammatical, and at the same time not contain very complicated grammatical constructions. Whether or not an MT system uses explicit grammatical rules in order to parse the input, correct, uncomplicated sentences are always easier to translate

Some MT systems use linguistic knowledge to analyse the input sentences, others do not. In both cases correct, uncomplicated input sentences will enhance the translation performance because unnecessary translation problems are avoided. For example, the second piece of text below is more likely to be successfully translated than the first:

(3)   a.   New toner units are held level during installation and, since they do not
           as supplied contain toner, must be filled prior to installation from a toner
           cartridge.
      b.   Fill the new toner unit with toner from a toner cartridge. Hold the new
           toner unit level while you put it in the printer.

The subclauses in the first sentence have been separated out as independent sentences in the second piece of text. The latter gives the instructions as a simple series of imperatives, ordered in the same way as the operations themselves.

The two final points in the list of writing rules prevent mistranslations by reducing potential sources of ambiguity. Many MT systems can do a reasonable job of selecting a correct interpretation of an ambiguous word in some circumstances, but they are unlikely to do this successfully in all cases. (For example, ETRANS failed to get the correct interpretation of the two different occurrences of *Seite* (i.e. 'side' or 'page') in the passage above.) Problems of ambiguity are extensively discussed in later chapters.

Restricting MT input according to simple writing rules like the ones given above can greatly enhance the performance of an MT system. But this is not the only advantage: it can also improve the understandability of a text for human readers. This is a desirable feature in, for example, technical texts and instruction manuals. As a consequence, several large companies have developed and extended the idea of writing rules, including limited vocabulary, in order to produce restricted forms of English suitable for technical texts. These restricted forms are known as *controlled languages*. We will discuss controlled languages in detail in Chapter 8.

In the past few years special tools have become available for supporting the production of text according to certain writing rules. There are spelling checkers and grammar checkers which can highlight words that are spelled incorrectly, or grammatical errors. There are also **critiquing systems** which analyse the text produced by an author and indicate where it deviates from the norms of the language. For example, given the example above of an over-complex sentence in a printer manual, such a tool might produce the following output:

Text Critique

New toner units are held level during installation and, since they do not as supplied contain toner, must be filled prior to installation from a toner cartridge.

sentence too long.
Since — disallowed clause in middle of sentence.
prior — disallowed word.
during installation — disallowed use of word: installation.

This is a rather sophisticated analysis of various violations found in the sentence. The controlled language this critiquing system is designed for only sanctions the word *installation* if it refers to some concrete object, as in *Remove the forward wheel hydraulic installation*; in this particular case *installation* is being used to denote the process of installing something. For the time being, this type of analysis is too advanced for most critiquing systems, which would find the sentence too difficult to analyse and would simply note that it is too long, not analysable, and contains the unknown word *prior*.

Critiquing systems ensure that texts are written according to a set of writing rules or the rules of a controlled language and thus help to catch errors which might upset an MT system. As a consequence they reduce the amount of time necessary for post-editing machine translated texts. They also reduce the time that someone else would normally have to spend on checking and revising the input text.

There is no theoretical reason why a controlled language critiquing system could not be completely integrated with an MT system designed to handle the controlled language — so that the translation system itself produces the critique while analysing the text for the purpose of translation. In fact, if the MT system and the critiquing system are completely separate, then the same piece of text will always have to be analysed twice — once by the critiquing system and a second time by the MT system. Moreover, the separation means that the same controlled language rules and electronic dictionary entries are repeated twice — once for each component. This makes it more expensive to revise or alter the controlled language. For these reasons, we can expect that MT system suppliers will seek to integrate controlled language critiquing and controlled language MT as closely as possible.

Of course, in practice not all text submitted to MT systems is (or can be, or should be) written according to a set of writing rules. Although this is not necessarily problematic it should be borne in mind that the less a text conforms to the rules mentioned above, the worse the raw translation output is likely to be. There will be a cutoff point where the input text is so badly written or so complicated that the raw output requires an uneconomically large amount of post-editing effort. In this case it may be possible to rewrite the problematic sentences in the input text or it may prove simplest to do the whole thing by hand.

2.4   The Translation Process

In the scenario we sketched above, the source text or some selected portion thereof was passed to the translation system which then produced raw translated output without any further human intervention. In fact, this is merely one of many ways the translation step can proceed.

2.4.1   Dictionary-Based Translation Support Tools

One point to bear in mind is that translation support can be given without actually providing full automatic translation. All MT systems are linked to electronic dictionaries which, for the present discussion, we can regard as sophisticated variants of their paper cousins. Such electronic dictionaries can be of immense help even if they are supplied or used without automatic translation of text. Here is one possible scenario:

> You are translating a text by hand. Using a mouse or the keyboard, you click on a word in the source text and a list of its possible translations is shown on screen. You click on the possible translation which seems most appropriate in the context and it is inserted directly into the target language text. Since you usually do this before you start typing in the translation of the sentence which contains the unknown work, the inserted word is inserted in the middle of an otherwise blank target language sentence. You then type in the rest of the translation around this inserted word.

Since technical texts typically contain contain large number of terms, and their preferred translations are not always remembered by the translator, this simple form of support can save a lot of time. It also helps to ensure that terms are consistently translated.

This *click to see, click to insert* facility is useful in dealing with low-frequency words in the source text. In technical text, technical terms — which can be complex multi-word units such as *faceplate delivery hose clip* — will usually have only one translation in the target language. If the electronic dictionary has a list of terms and their translations, those translations can be directly inserted into the target text. This gives the following scenario:

You are translating a technical text by hand. You click on the icon *Term Support* and all the source language terms in the current text unit which are recognised as being in the electronic term dictionary are highlighted. A second click causes all the translations of those terms to be inserted in otherwise empty target language sentences. You then type in the rest of the translation around each inserted term.

Dictionary-based translation support tools of this sort depend on two things:

1 The required terms and words must be available in the electronic dictionary. This may well require that they were put there in the first place by translators in the organization using the tool.

2 There must be some simple means for dealing with the inflections on the ends of words since the form of a word or term in the text may not be the same as the cited form in the dictionary. As a simple example, the text may contain the plural form *faceplate delivery hose clips* rather than the singular form kept in the dictionary. The problem is more complex with verb inflections and in languages other than English.

These and other issues concerning the MT dictionary will be discussed in Chapter 5.

Translation Aids in the Workplace No. 72:
Automatic Lexical Lookup

2.4.2   Interaction in Translation

MT systems analyse text and must decide what its structure is. In most MT systems, where there are doubts and uncertainties about the structure, or about the correct choice of word for a translation, they are resolved by appeal to in-built *rules-of-thumb* — which may well be wrong for a particular case. It has often been suggested that MT systems could usefully interact with translators by pausing from time to time to ask simple questions about translation problems.

Another sort of interaction could occur when the system has problems in choosing a correct source language analysis; a good analysis is needed to ensure good translation. For example, suppose that a printer manual being translated from English contains the following sentence:

(4)   Attach the printer to the PC with a parallel interface cable.

The question is: are we talking about a particular type of PC (personal computer) which comes with a *parallel interface cable* (whatever that is) or any old PC which can be connected to the printer by means of an independent *parallel interface cable*? In the first case, the *with*, in the phrase *with a parallel interface cable* means *having* or *fitted with* and modifies the noun *PC*, whilst in the second it means *using* and modifies the verb *attach*. One good reason for worrying about the choice is because in many languages *with* will be translated differently for the two cases. Faced with such an example, an MT system might ask on screen exactly the same question:

(5)   Does with a parallel interface cable modify the PC or does it modify
           Attach ?

Another sort of analysis question arises with pronouns. Consider translating the following:

(6)   Place the paper in the paper tray and replace the cover. Ensure that it
           is completely closed.

Does *it* in the second sentence refer to *the paper*, *the paper tray*, or *the cover*? The decision matters because the translation of *it* in many languages will vary depending on the gender of the expression it refers back to. Making such a decision depends on rather subtle knowledge, such as the fact that covers, but not trays or paper are typical things to be closed, which is hard perhaps impossible to build into an MT system. However, it is the sort of question that a human translator may be able to answer.

The following is a possible scenario:

> You are translating a text interactively with an MT system. The system displays the source text in one window, while displaying the target text as it is produced in another. On encountering the word *it*, the system parses, highlights the words *paper*, *paper tray*, and *cover* in the first sentence, and asks you to click on the one which is the antecedent (i.e. the one *it* refers back to). It is then able to choose the appropriate form of the translation, and it proceeds with the rest of the sentence.

It is hardly surprising that a machine may need to ask such questions because the answers may not be at all clear, in some cases even for a human translator. With poorly written technical texts, it may even be the case that only the author knows.

2.5 Document Revision

The main factor which decides the amount of post-editing that needs to be done on a translation produced by machine is of course the quality of the output. But this itself depends on the requirements of the client, in particular (a) the translation aim and (b) the time available. In the case of the printer manual in the scenario above the translation aim was to provide a printer manual in English for export purposes. The fact that the translation was going to be widely distributed outside the organization required it to be of high quality — a correct, well-written and clear piece of English text, which means thorough and conscientious post-editing.

The opposite situation occurs when a rough and ready translation is needed out of some language for personal or internal use, perhaps only to get the gist of some incoming text to see if it looks interesting enough for proper translation. (If it is not, little time or money or effort has been wasted finding out). Here is the sort of scenario in which it might work:

> You are an English-speaking agronomist monitoring a stream of information on cereal crop diseases coming in over global computer networks in four different languages. You have a fast MT system which is hooked into the network and translates — extremely badly — from three of the languages into English. Looking at the output and using your experience of the sort of things that reports contain, you should be able to get enough of an idea to know whether to ignore it or pass it on to your specialist translators.

Of course, in this situation it is the speed of the MT system, not its quality that matters — a very simple system that does no more than transliterate and translate a few of the words may even be enough.

We've now looked at two cases: one in which full post-editing needed to be done, one in which no post-editing whatsoever was required. Another option could be to do some post-editing on a translation in order to make it easy to read and understand, but without having the perfection of a published text in mind. Most post-editors are also translators and are used to producing high quality texts. They are likely to apply the same sort of output standards to their translations produced automatically. Though this policy is very desirable for, for instance, business correspondence and manuals, it is not at all necessary to reach the same sort of standard for internal electronic mail. Some MT output could be subject to a *rough and ready* post-edit — where the post-editor tries to remove or adjust only the grossest errors and incomprehensibilities — rather than the usual thorough and painstaking job. The main advantage of this option is that translator time is saved. Even if documents are occasionally sent back for re-translation or re-editing, the *rough and ready* post-edit policy might still save money overall. Again, the factors of translation aim and time available play an important role.

MT systems make the same sorts of translation mistake time and time again. Sometimes these errors can be eliminated by modifying the information in the dictionary. Other sorts of errors may stem from subtle problems in the system's grammars or linguistic processing strategies which cannot ordinarily be resolved without specialist knowledge. Once an error pattern has been recognised, a translator can scan text looking for just such errors. If the error is just a matter of consistently mistranslating one word or string of words, then — as in the scenario — the ordinary search-and-replace tools familiar from word processors will be of some help. In general, since the errors one will find in machine translated texts are different from those one finds in other texts, specialized word processor commands may be helpful. For example, commands which transpose words, or at a more sophisticated level, ones which change the form of a single word, or all the words in a certain region from masculine to feminine, or singular to plural, might be useful post-editing tools.

The imaginary company that we have been discussing in the previous sections deals with large volumes of similar, technical text. This text similarity allows the MT system to be tuned in various ways, so as to achieve the best possible performance on one particular type of text on one particular topic. An illustration of this can be found in the section heading of our example text *Einstellung der Druckdichte*. The German word *Einstellung* can have several translations: *employment, discontinuation, adjustment* and *attitude*. Since we are dealing here with technical texts we can discard the first and last possible translations. Of the two translations left, *adjustment*, is the most common one in this text type, and the computer dictionaries as originally supplied have been updated accordingly. The tuning of a system takes time and effort, but will in the long run save post-editing time.

Obviously enough, the difficulty of post-editing and the time required for it correlates with the quality of the raw MT output: the worse the output, the greater the post-edit effort. For one thing, the post-editor will need to refer more and more to the source language text when the output gets less intelligible. Even though this seems to be a major drawback at the beginning, bear in mind that post-editors will get used to the typical error patterns of the MT system; MT output that may seem unintelligible at the beginning will require less reference to the source language text after some time. Familiarity with the pattern of errors produced by a particular MT system is thus an important factor in reducing post-editing time. More generally, familiarity with the document processing environment used for post-editing and its particular facilities is an important time saver.

2.6 Summary

This chapter has given a picture of how MT might be used in an imaginary company, and looked in outline at the typical stages of translation: *document preparation*, *translation* (including various kinds of human involvement and *interaction*), and *document revision*, and at the various skills and tools required. In doing this we have tried also to give an idea of some of the different situations in which MT can be useful. In particular, the case of 'gist' translation, where speed is important, and quality less important, compared to the case where a translation is intended for widespread publication, and the quality of the finished (post-edited) product is paramount. These are all matters we will return to in the following chapters.

2.7 Further Reading

Descriptions of how MT is actually used in corporate settings can be found in the Proceedings of the Aslib Conferences (normally subtitled *Translating and the Computer*) which we mentioned in the Further Reading section of Chapter 1.

For readers interested in finding out more about the practicalities of pre- and post-editing , there are several relevant contribution in [Vasconcellos, 1988], in [Lawson, 1982a]. There is a useful discussion of issues in pre-editing and text preparation, in [Pym, 1990], and we will say more about some related issues in Chapter 8.

An issue that we have not addressed specifically in this chapter is that of machine aids to (human) translation, such as on-line and automatic dictionaries and terminological databases, multilingual word processors, and so on. We will say more about terminological databases in Chapter 5. Relevant discussion of interaction between machine (and machine aided) translation systems and human users can be found in [Vasconcellos, 1988],[Stoll, 1988],[Knowles, 1990] and various papers by Alan Melby, including [Melby, 1987; Melby, 1992], who discusses the idea of a 'translator's workbench'. In fact, it should be clear that there is no really hard and fast line that can be drawn between such things and the sort of MT system we have described here. For one thing, an adequate MT system should clearly include such aids in addition to anything else. In any case, in the kind of setting we have described, there is a sense in which even an MT system which produces very high quality output is really serving as a translators' aid, since it is helping improve their productivity by producing draft translations. What are sometimes called distinction between 'Machine Aided Human Translation', 'Human Aided Machine Translation', and 'Machine Translation' *per se* actually form a continuum.

Chapter 3

Representation and Processing

3.1   Introduction

In this chapter we will introduce some of the techniques that can be used to represent the kind of information that is needed for translation in such a way that it can be processed automatically. This will provide some necessary background for Chapter 4, where we describe how MT systems actually work.

Human Translators actually deploy at least five distinct kinds of knowledge:

- Knowledge of the source language.

- Knowledge of the target language. This allows them to produce texts that are acceptable in the target language.

- Knowledge of various correspondences between source language and target language (at the simplest level, this is knowledge of how individual words can be translated).

- Knowledge of the subject matter, including ordinary general knowledge and 'common sense'. This, along with knowledge of the source language, allows them to understand what the text to be translated means.

- Knowledge of the culture, social conventions, customs, and expectations, etc. of the speakers of the source and target languages.

This last kind of knowledge is what allows translators to act as genuine mediators, ensuring that the target text genuinely communicates the same sort of message, and has the same sort of impact on the reader, as the source text.[1] Since no one has

---

[1] Hatim and Mason [Hatim and Mason, 1990] give a number of very good examples where translation requires this sort of cultural mediation.

the remotest idea how to represent or manipulate this sort of knowledge, we will not pursue it here — except to note that it is the lack of this sort of knowledge that makes us think that the proper role of MT is the production of draft or 'literal' translations.

Knowledge of the target language is important because without it, what a human or automatic translator produces will be ungrammatical, or otherwise unacceptable. Knowledge of the source language is important because the first task of the human translator is to figure out what the words of the source text mean (without knowing what they mean it is not generally possible to find their equivalent in the target language).

It is usual to distinguish several kinds of linguistic knowledge:

- Phonological knowledge: knowledge about the sound system of a language, knowledge which, for example, allows one to work out the likely pronunciation of novel words. When dealing with written texts, such knowledge is not particularly useful. However, there is related knowledge about **orthography** which can be useful. Knowledge about spelling is an obvious example.

- Morphological knowledge: knowledge about how words can be constructed: that *printer* is made up of *print + er*.

- Syntactic knowledge: knowledge about how sentences, and other sorts of phrases can be made up out of words.

- Semantic knowledge: knowledge about what words and phrases mean, about how the meaning of a phrase is related to the meaning of its component words.

Some of this knowledge is knowledge about individual words, and is represented in dictionaries. For example, the fact that the word *print* is spelled the way it is, that it is not made up of other words, that it is a verb, that it has a meaning related to that of the verb *write*, and so on. This, along with issues relating to the nature and use of morphological knowledge, will be discussed in Chapter 5.

However, some of the knowledge is about whole classes or **categories** of word. In this chapter, we will focus on this sort of knowledge about syntax and semantics. Sections 3.2.1, and 3.2.2 discuss syntax, issues relating to semantics are considered in Section 3.2.3. We will look first on how syntactic knowledge of the source and target languages can be expressed so that a machine can use it. In the second part of the chapter, we will look at how this knowledge can be used in automatic processing of human language.

3.2   Representing Linguistic Knowledge

In general, syntax is concerned with two slightly different sorts of analysis of sentences. The first is **constituent** or **phrase structure** analysis — the division of sentences into their constituent parts and the categorization of these parts as nominal, verbal, and so on. The second is to do with **grammatical relations**; the assignment of grammatical relations such as SUBJECT, OBJECT, HEAD and so on to various parts of the sentence. We will discuss these in turn.

3.2.1   Grammars and Constituent Structure

Sentences are made up of words, traditionally categorised into **parts of speech** or **categories** including nouns, verbs, adjectives, adverbs and prepositions (normally abbreviated to N, V, A, ADV, and P). A **grammar** of a language is a set of rules which says how these parts of speech can be put together to make grammatical, or 'well-formed' sentences.

For English, these rules should indicate that (1a) is grammatical, but that (1b) is not (we indicate this by marking it with a '*').

(1)   a.   Put some paper in the printer.
      b.   *Printer some put the in paper.

Here are some simple rules for English grammar, with examples. A **sentence** consists of a **noun phrase**, such as *the user* followed by a **modal** or an **auxiliary verb**, such as *should*, followed by a **verb phrase**, such as *clean the printer.*

(2)   The user should clean the printer.

A **noun phrase** can consist of a **determiner**, or **article**, such as *the*, or *a*, and a **noun**, such as *printer* (3a). In some circumstances, the determiner can be omitted (3b).

(3)   a.   the printer
      b.   printers

'Sentence', is often abbreviated to S, 'noun phrase' to NP, 'verb phrase' to VP, 'auxiliary' to AUX, and 'determiner' to DET. This information is easily visualized by means of a labelled bracketing of a string of words, as follows, or as a **tree diagram**, as in Figure 3.1.

(4)   a.   Users should clean the printer.
      b. $[_S [_{NP} [_N$ users $]][_{AUX}$ should $][_{VP} [_V$ clean $][_{NP} [_{DET}$ the $][_N$ printer $]]]]$

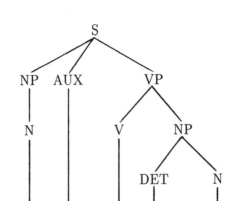

Figure 3.1 A Tree Structure for a Simple Sentence

The auxiliary verb is optional, as can be seen from (5), and the verb phrase can consist of just a verb (such as *stopped*):

(5)   a.   The printer should stop.
      b.   The printer stopped.

NP and VP can contain **prepositional phrases** (PPs), made up of **prepositions** (*on, in, with*, etc.) and NPs:

(6)   a.   The printer stops on occasions .
      b.   Put the cover on the printer .
      c.   Clean the printer with a cloth .

The reader may recall that traditional grammar distinguishes between **phrases** and **clauses**. The phrases in the examples above are parts of the sentence which cannot be used by themselves to form independent sentences. Taking *The printer stopped*, neither its NP nor its VP can be used as independent sentences:

(7)   a.   *The printer
      b.   *Stopped

By contrast, many types of clause can stand as independent sentences. For example, (8a) is a sentence which consists of a single clause — *The printer stopped*. As the bracketing indicates, (8b) consists of two clauses co-ordinated by *and*. The sentence

(8c) also consists of two clauses, one (*that the printer stops*) embedded in the other, as a sentential **complement** of the verb.

(8)   a.   [$_S$ The printer stopped]

      b.   [$_S$ [$_S$ The printer stopped]and [$_S$ the warning light went on]].

      c.   [$_S$ You will observe [$_S$ that the printer stops]].

There is a wide range of criteria that linguists use for deciding whether something is a phrase, and if it is, what sort of phrase it is, what category it belongs to. As regards the first issue, the leading idea is that phrases consist of classes of words which normally group together. If we consider example (2) again (*The user should clean the printer*), one can see that there are good reasons for grouping *the* and *user* together as a phrase, rather than grouping *user* and *should*. The point is *the* and *user* can be found together in many other contexts, while *user* and *should* cannot.

(9)   a.   A full set of instructions are supplied to the user .

      b.   The user must clean the printer with care.

      c.   It is the user who is responsible for day-to-day maintenance.

      d.   *User should clean the printer.

As regards what category a phrase like *the user* belongs to, one can observe that it contains a noun as its 'chief' element (one can omit the determiner more easily than the noun), and the positions it occurs in are also the positions where one gets proper nouns (e.g. names such as *Sam*). This is not to say that questions about constituency and category are all clear cut. For example, we have supposed that auxiliary verbs are part of the sentence, but not part of the VP. One could easily find arguments to show that this is wrong, and that *should clean the printer* should be a VP, just like *clean the printer*, giving a structure like the following, and Figure 3.2:

(10)   [$_S$ [$_{NP}$ [$_N$ users]][$_{VP}$ [$_{AUX}$ should][$_V$ clean][$_{NP}$ [$_{DET}$ the][$_N$ printer]]]]

Moreover, from a practical point of view, making the right assumptions about constituency can be important, since making wrong ones can lead to having to write grammars that are much more complex than otherwise. For example, suppose that we decided that determiners and nouns did not, in fact, form constituents. Instead of being able to say that a sentence is an NP followed by an auxiliary, followed by a VP, we would have to say that it was a determiner followed by an noun, followed by a VP. This may not seem like much, but notice that we would have to complicate the rules we gave for VP and for PP in the same way. Not only this, but our rule for NP is rather simplified, since we have not allowed for adjectives before the noun, or PPs after the noun. So everywhere we could have written 'NP', we would have to write something very much longer. In practice, we would quickly see that our grammar was unnecessarily complex, and simplify it by introducing something like an NP constituent.

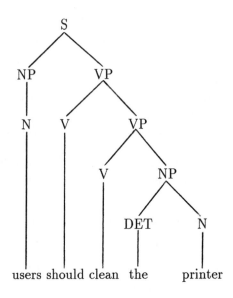

Figure 3.2 An Alternative Analysis

For convenience linguists often use a special notation to write out grammar rules. In this notation, a rule consists of a 'left-hand-side' (LHS) and a 'right-hand-side' (RHS) connected by an arrow (→):

```
S  → NP (AUX) VP

VP → V (NP) PP*

NP → (DET) (ADJ) N PP*

PP → P NP

N  → user

N  → users

N  → printer

N  → printers

V  → clean

V  → cleans
```

```
AUX  →  should

DET  →  the

DET  →  a

P  →  with
```

The first rule says that a Sentence can be rewritten as (or decomposes into, or consists of) an NP followed by an optional AUX, followed by VP (optionality is indicated by brackets). Another rule says that a PP can consist of a P and an NP. Looked at the other way, the first rule can be interpreted as saying that an NP, and AUX and a VP make up a sentence. Items marked with a star ("*") can appear any number of times (including zero) — so the second rule allows there to be any number of PPs in a VP. The rules with 'real words' like *user* on their RHS serve as a sort of primitive dictionary. Thus the first one says that *user* is a noun, the fifth one that *clean* is a verb. Since the NP rule says that an N by itself can make up an NP, we can also infer that *printers* is an NP, and since (by the VP rule) a V and an NP make up a VP, *clean printers* is a VP. Thus, a grammar such as this gives information about what the constituents of a sentence are, and what categories they belong to, in the same way as our informal rules at the start of the section.

Returning to the tree representation in Figure 3.1, each node in the tree (and each bracketed part of the string representation) corresponds to the LHS of a particular rule, while the daughters of each node correspond to the RHS of that rule. If the RHS has two constituents, as in NP → DET N, there will be two branches and two daughters; if there are three constitituents, there will be three branches and three daughters, and so on.

It is worthwhile to have some terminology for talking about trees. Looking from the top,[2] the trees above start from (or 'are rooted in') a sentence node — the LHS of our sentence rule. Near the bottom of the trees, we have a series of nodes corresponding to the LHS's of dictionary rules and, immediately below them at the very bottom of the trees, actual words from the corresponding RHS's of the dictionary rules. These are called the 'leaves' or terminal nodes of the tree. It is normal to speak of 'mother' nodes and 'daughter' nodes (e.g. the S node is the mother of the NP, AUX, and VP nodes), and of mothers 'dominating' daughters. In practice most sentences are longer and more complicated than our example. If we add adjectives and prepositional phrases, and some more words, more complex trees can be produced, as shown in Figure 3.3, where the NP which is the left daughter of the S node contains an adjective and a noun but no determiner (the NP rule in our grammar above allows for noun phrases of this form), the NP in VP contains a determiner and a PP.

A large collection of such rules will constitute a formal grammar for a language —

---

[2] For some reason, linguists' trees are always written upside down, with the 'root' at the top, and the leaves (the actual words) at the bottom.

formal, because it attempts to give a mathematically precise account of what it is for a sentence to be grammatical. As well as being more concise than the informal descriptions at the beginning of the section, the precision of formal grammars is an advantage when it comes to providing computational treatments.

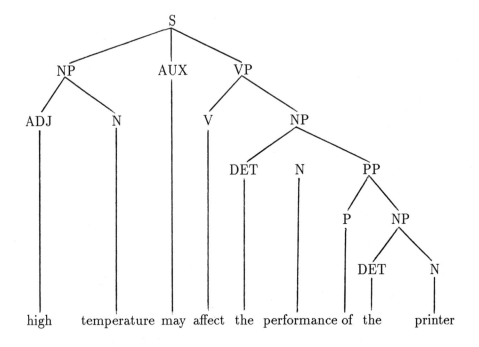

Figure 3.3 A More Complex Tree Structure

We should emphasise that the little grammar we have given is not the *only* possible grammar for the fragment of English it is supposed to describe. The question of which grammar is 'best' is a matter for investigation. One question is that of completeness – does the grammar describe *all* sentences of the language? In this respect, one can see that our example above is woefully inadequate. Another issue is whether a grammar is correct in the sense of allowing only sentences that are in fact grammatical: our example grammar falls down in this respect, since it allows the examples in (11), among many others.

(11) a.   *User cleans.

b.   *Users cleans printers.

c.   *Users should cleans printers.

A grammar may also be incorrect in associating constituents with the wrong categories. For example, as we noted above, one would probably prefer a grammar which recognizes that determiners and nouns make up NPs, and that the NP that occur in S (i.e. subject NPs) and those that appear in VP (object NPs) are the same (as our grammar does) to a grammar which treats them as belonging to different categories — this would suggest (wrongly) that there are things that can appear as subjects, but not as objects, and vice versa. This is obviously not true, except for some pronouns that can appear as subjects but not as objects: *I, he, she*, etc. A worse defect of this kind is the treatment of words – the grammar gives far too little information about them, and completely misses the fact that *clean*, and *cleans* are actually different forms of the same verb. We will show how this problem can be overcome in Chapter 5.

In a practical context, a further issue is how easy it is to understand the grammar, and to modify it (by extending it, or fixing mistakes), and how easy it is to use it for automatic processing (an issue to which we will return). Of course, all these matters are often related.

3.2.2 Further Analysis: Grammatical Relations

So far we have talked about the kind of grammatical knowledge that can be expressed in terms of a constituent structure tree — information about the constituent units, and the parts of speech. But there are other kinds of information implicit in these representations which it is useful to make explicit. In particular, information about which phrases fulfil which grammatical relations or **grammatical functions** such as SUBJECT, OBJECT and SENTENTIAL COMPLEMENT. English SUB-JECTs are normally the NPs which come before the verb, and OBJECTs normally occur immediately after the verb. In other languages these relations may be realised differently with respect to the verb. For example, in Japanese the normal word order is SUBJECT OBJECT VERB, and in Irish and Welsh it is VERB SUBJECT OB-JECT. In many languages, such as Russian, the VERB, SUBJECT and OBJECT can appear in essentially any order. (In such languages the different grammatical relations can often be recognized by different forms of the noun – usually called **cases**. In English, this only occurs with pronouns — *he, she*, etc., are only possible as SUBJECTs). What this suggests, of course, is that while the constituent structures of languages differ greatly, they may appear more similar when described in terms of grammatical relations.

Phrases which serve as SUBJECT, OBJECT, etc., should also be distinguished from those which serve as MODIFIERs, or ADJUNCTs, of various sorts. For example, in the sentence (12) *You* is the SUBJECT of the verb *clean, the printer casing* is its OBJECT, whilst the prepositional phrases *with a non-abrasive compound* and *at any time* are ADJUNCTs.

(12)   You can clean the printer casing with a non-abrasive compound at any time.

ADJUNCTs are prototypically optional — unlike SUBJECTs. For example, a sentence which omits them is still perfectly well formed: there is nothing wrong with (13a), but omitting the SUBJECT, as illustrated in (13b) produces an ungrammatical result.[3]

(13) a. You can clean the printer casing.

      b. *Can clean the printer casing.

There are various ways of representing sentences in terms of grammatical relations, but it is essentially not very different from that of constituent structure tree representation, which we have seen earlier in this chapter. The basic idea is to represent sentences in terms of their constituent parts (so a tree representation is convenient), but since one wants to represent the grammatical relation which the parts have to the whole, it is common to mark either the branches or the nodes with the appropriate relation. Figure 3.4 gives a representation of (14). This can be compared with a constituent structure representation for the same sentence in Figure 3.5.

(14)   The temperature has affected the printer.

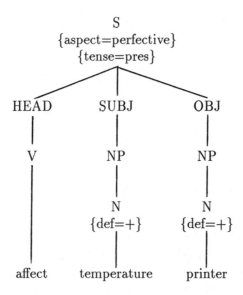

Figure 3.4 A Representation of Grammatical Relations

In Figure 3.4, the relations are marked on the nodes, and a new relation HEAD has been introduced. The HEAD element is, intuitively, the most important element

---

[3]In English, SUBJECTs can only be omitted in imperative sentences, for example orders, such as *Clean the printer regularly*, and in some embedded sentences, e.g. the boxed part of *It is essential* | *to clean the printer* |

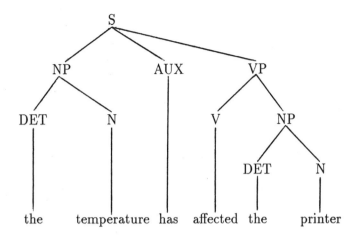

Figure 3.5 A Constituent Structure Representation

from the point of view of the grammar of the whole phrase — the element which makes the phrase what it is. This is the noun in an NP, the verb in a VP or sentence, the preposition in a PP.

There are three important differences between this tree representing grammatical relations, and those representing constituent structure. First, instead of consisting of an NP, and a VP (containing a V and an NP), the representation of grammatical relations consists of a V and two NPs – the VP node has disappeared. Second, in this grammatical relations representation, the order of the branches is unimportant. This is possible, of course, because the grammatical relations have been indicated and this gives information about word order implicitly. Figure 3.4 could be redrawn with the branches in any order, and it would still be a representation of *The temperature affects the printer*, since this is the only sentence that has these items with these relations. By contrast, reordering the branches in a constituent structure tree might produce a representation of a quite different sentence, or no sentence at all.

The third difference is that some of the words have been missed out from Figure 3.4, and have been replaced by **features**, that is, pairs that consist of an **attribute**, such as def, tense, and aspect, and a **value**, such as +, pres, and perfective. The features aspect=perfective and tense=pres indicate that the sentence as a whole is in the present perfect tense. It is called perfect because it is used to describe events or actions that have been 'perfected' or completed, unlike, for example, a sentence such as *The temperature was affecting the printer*, where the 'affecting' is still going on at the time the writer is referring to. It is called *present* perfect because the auxiliary verb is in a present tense form (*has* not *had*). The feature def=+ on the NPs means these NPs are definite. This definiteness indicates that the writer and reader have some particular object of the appropriate kind in mind. Compare, for example, *The printer has stopped* where one particular printer which is in some sense known to both writer and reader is being discussed, with *A printer has stopped*, where this is not the case.

These three differences are all intended to represent what is expressed by the sentence, abstracting away from the *way* it is expressed: we abstract away from the division into NP and VP, from the particular word order, and from the way in which the definiteness of the NPs and the tense and aspect of the sentence are realized (in English it is by the determiners, and the auxiliary verb respectively; in other languages it might be realized differently).

When it comes to describing the relationship between constituent structure, and what we might call relational structures, such as Figure 3.4, there are basically two approaches. One is simply to add information about grammatical relations to the grammar rules.

```
S  → NP{SUBJECT} AUX VP{HEAD}

VP → V{HEAD} NP{OBJECT} PP{ADJUNCT}*

AUX → has{aspect=perfective, tense=pres}
```

The idea is that these annotations can be interpreted in such a way that a representation like Figure 3.4 can be constructed at the same time as the constituent structure tree. To do this requires a convention to 'flatten' the constituent structure tree 'merging' a structure (e.g. the structure of S) that is associated with the LHS of a rule with that of the HEAD daughter on the RHS, and a convention which simply merges in information that comes from items which do not have a grammatical relation, such as the AUX.

A second approach is to have special rules which relate the constituent structure representation to the representation of grammatical relations. One such rule might look like this:

```
[s NP:$1, AUX:$2, [vp V:$3, NP:$4 ]]
↔
[s HEAD:$3, SUBJ:$1, OBJ:$4 ]
```

In this rule, $1, $2, etc. are **variables**, or temporary names for pieces of structure. The idea is that such a rule matches a constituent structure such as that in Figure 3.3, and assigns (or 'binds') the variables to various pieces of structure. For example the NP containing *temperature* becomes bound to the variable $1. The rule can then be interpreted as an instruction to transform the constituent structure tree into a tree like Figure 3.4. This involves making this NP into the SUBJECT, making the V into the HEAD, and missing out the AUX entirely, among other things. The rule is rather simplified, of course, since it does not mention putting the information about perfective aspect into the grammatical relation representation, and ignores the problem of dealing with PPs, but it should give some idea.

The reader may also notice that the arrow used in this rule is bidirectional. This is intended to suggest that the rule simply states a correspondence between constituent structure, and grammatical relation representations, without suggesting that one is prior to the other. Thus, the idea is that one could equally well use the rule to transform Figure 3.4 into Figure 3.5 and vice versa. Similarly, the annotation approach is not supposed to be directional (though this may be somewhat harder to appreciate).

Many verbs have what are called **active** and **passive** forms, as in the following.

(15) a. Temperature affects │printers│. (*Active*)

   b. │Printers│ are affected by temperature. (*Passive*)

Notice that the object in the active sentence corresponds to the subject in the passive. This raises the question of what the grammatical relations SUBJECT and OBJECT should mean. One possibility is to use the the terms in the sense of the 'surface' grammatical relations. The SUBJECTs of actives and the corresponding passives would be different, then. In particular, *temperature* would be the SUBJECT of (15a), and *printers* would be the SUBJECT of (15b). The alternative is to adopt a notion of a *deep* relation which picks out the same elements in both active and passive sentence. We would then say that (in English) the D-OBJECT ('deep' OBJECT) corresponds to the noun phrase after the verb in active sentences and to the noun phrase that precedes the verb in the corresponding passive. In active sentences, the surface and deep relations are the same, but they are different in passives, as can be seen from the following (in the passive sentence there is no surface OBJECT, and the D-SUBJECT has become a sort of ADJUNCT, in a PP with the preposition *by*).

(16) a. Temperature affects printers. (*Active*)
         SUBJECT = *temperature*, OBJECT = *printers*
         D-SUBJECT = *temperature*, D-OBJECT = *printers*

   b. Printers are affected by temperature. (*Passive*)
         SUBJECT = *printers*, OBJECT = 0,
         D-SUBJECT = *temperature* D-OBJECT = *printers*

Interpreting SUBJECT as deep subject is clearly consistent with the general idea of abstracting away from surface characteristics in the grammatical relational representation. But it is not obviously the right move to make. For example, English verbs often vary their form depending on the nature of their subject (this is called **agreement** – as the following makes clear, there is also agreement of demonstratives like *this/these* with their head noun).

(17) a. These factors affect printers.

   b. This factor affects printers.

   c. *These factors affects printers.

   d. *This factor affect printers.

However, the point to notice is that the agreement is with the surface subject, not the deep subject. Thus, if one wants to use a representation of grammatical relations to describe the phenomenon of agreement, the notion of SUBJECT had better be surface subject. This is not, in itself, a critical point here. The point we are making is simply that there is a range of options, and that the option chosen can make a difference for the overall description.

3.2.3 Meaning

Representing information about grammar in the form of grammar rules is useful in two ways in MT. First, as will become clear in the Chapter 4, it is possible to use the sort of linguistic representation that the rules provide to get simpler, and better descriptions of what is involved in translation, by abstracting away from some superficial differences between languages – as we have noted the abstract representations of sentences in different languages are often more similar than the sentences themselves. But one can also use such representations as the basis for still more abstract representations of meaning. Working out the meaning of sentences is an important part of the translation process for human translators, and the ability to work out the meaning — to 'understand' (in some sense) the source text would allow an MT system to produce much better translations. This may sound an impossible task, and perhaps at some level it is. However, there is another, less ambitious, level where automatic 'understanding' is possible. In this section we will look at what this involves in a preliminary way (we will say more about it in Chapter 7).

It is useful to think of 'understanding' as involving three kinds of knowledge:

1 **Semantic** knowledge. This is knowledge of what expressions (individual words and sentences) mean, independent of the context they appear in.

2 **Pragmatic** knowledge. This is knowledge of what expressions mean in situations and particular occasions of use.

3 **Real world**, or common sense knowledge.

Consider the following example:

(18)   The user may prefer to clean the printer every week with a non-corrosive fluid. Do not use abrasive or corrosive solvents, as this may harm its appearance.

One thing that is involved in understanding the meaning of this is working out the different **semantic relations** that the different NPs have to the predicates. For example, *a non-corrosive fluid* is understood as an *instrument* to be used in cleaning, *every week* indicates the time period in which the cleaning should be repeated, *the printer* denotes the thing to be cleaned, and *the user* denotes both the entity that has a preference, and which performs the cleaning. This is *semantic* information, because it is information that this sentence would convey on any occasion of use. However, recovering this information is not enough to 'understand' the example. One must also be able to work out that these sentences — or at least the second sentence — is to be understood as a *warning* not to do something. In this case, the form of the sentence is a fairly clear guide to this, but this is not always so. For example, sentences that are interrogative in form are often requests for information, but it is quite possible for such sentences to be interpreted as offers, requests for action, warnings, or as assertions (i.e. as giving information). This last case is what is called a rhetorical question; the following interrogatives might be interpreted in some of the other ways, depending on the context.

(19)   a.   Would you like some cake?

        b.   Don't you think it is cold in here?

        c.   Can't you see what you are doing to that printer?

Of course, the key words here are 'depending on the context'. Working out, for example, that (19b) is interpreted as a request for the speaker to close a window depends on many things in the context where it is uttered (it might also, for example, be a comment on the social atmosphere). The sort of knowledge of social and linguistic conventions involved here is part of what is normally thought of as pragmatic knowledge.

But even this is not enough to understand the example completely. For example, there are the pronouns *this*, and *it* in the second sentence. It is obvious (to the human reader) that *this* should be interpreted as cleaning with an abrasive or corrosive solvent, and that *it* should be interpreted as referring to the printer (i.e. the sense is: 'cleaning ... may harm the printer's appearance'). But this is not the only semantically and pragmatically possible interpretation. One could imagine the same sentence being uttered in a context where it is the appearance of the fluid that will be affected (imagine one is dealing with a precious fluid of some kind):

(20)   Do not place the fluid in sunlight, as this may harm its appearance.

What is involved here is real world, or common sense knowledge, perhaps the knowledge that if a corrosive fluid comes into contact with a printer (or something similar), it is the printer's appearance that is damaged. This is not knowledge about the meanings of the words, or about how language is used in different social contexts.

What You Say and What They Hear:
A Normal Conversation in the Linguistics Common Room

Similarly, consider the meaning of a word like *printers*. Semantic knowledge should supply the information that one interpretation of this refers to a collection of machines which perform the activity of printing, or perhaps to such things in general (as in *printers are expensive and unreliable*). Real world knowledge will indicate that the members of this collection are typically of a certain size (bigger than pencils, but smaller than houses, say), and have certain parts, and characteristic flaws. When someone utters the word *Printers!*, in an exasperated tone, with a piece of chewed up paper in their hand, you may realize that what they intend to convey is some quite complicated attitude, including annoyance. It is pragmatic knowledge that allows you to work out that this is their intention, and that they do not, for example, want you to go and buy them a number of printers.

Of course, the distinctions between these different kinds of knowledge are not always clear, and they interact in complex ways in determining how an utterance is actually understood. Nevertheless, the basic idea of the distinction should be clear.

How can this sort of information about sentences be represented? The representation of pragmatic and common sense or real world knowledge raises many difficult problems, and is not really necessary for understanding the discussion in the following chapters, so we will postpone discussion until Chapter 6. However, we will say something about semantic representations here.

One kind of semantic representation would provide different relation names, and indicate which NP had which relation. In the following example, which is a simplified part of (18) , one might have relations like INSTRUMENT, AGENT (for the user), and THEME or PATIENT (for the printer), giving a representation like Figure 3.6 These relations are sometimes called **semantic roles, (deep) cases,** or **thematic roles.**

(21)   The user cleans the printer with a non-abrasive solvent.

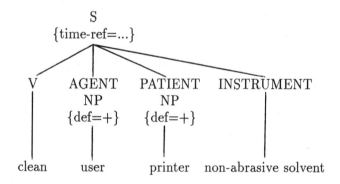

Figure 3.6 A Representation of Semantic Relations

Such a representation looks very much like Figure 3.4, except that the labels SUBJECT, OBJECT, etc. have been replaced by these thematic roles, and syntactic information about tense and aspect has been replaced by information about time reference.[4] The rules that relate these roles to grammatical relations would say things like "The AGENT will normally correspond to the SUBJECT of an active sentence, and an NP in a *by*-phrase in a passive sentence"; "The INSTRUMENT normally appears in a PP with the preposition *with*", "The PATIENT is very often the OBJECT of active sentences" However, there are some verbs which violate these general patterns. For example, they are very different with *like* and *please* – the PATIENT (*bright colours* in the following example) is normally the OBJECT of *like*, but the SUBJECT of *please*.

---

[4] We have not specified the time-reference information: see Chapter 7.

(22)   a.   Children like bright colours.

      b.   Bright colours please children.

The usefulness of a semantic representation is further explored in Chapter 7.

3.3   Processing

In the previous sections, we have tried to give an outline of some of the different kinds of knowledge that are needed in text understanding (and hence, translation), and how they can be represented. We will now give an idea of how this knowledge can be manipulated automatically. We will do this in two stages. First, we will look at what is called **analysis**, or **parsing**. This is the process of taking an input string of expressions, and producing representations of the kind we have seen in the previous section. Second, we will look at **synthesis**, or **generation**, which is the reverse process – taking a representation, and producing the corresponding sentence.

It may be helpful to point out at the beginning that though the representations we have given are generally graphic objects — trees or networks drawn with lines — these are not themselves the representations that the computer deals with. For example, the standard internal representation of a tree is as a **list**, containing sublists, with any labels on a node being represented as the first element of the list. If we write lists between '(' and ')', and separate elements with commas, then the tree representation given in Figure 3.1 would look as follows (in fact, we have already shown this sort of representation for linguistic trees).

(S, (NP, (N, users)), (AUX, should), (VP, (V, clean), (NP, (DET, the), (N, printer))))

Lists are one of the datastructures that can be represented and manipulated very easily within a computer.

3.3.1   Parsing

The task of an automatic parser is to take a formal grammar and a sentence and apply the grammar to the sentence in order to (a) check that it is indeed grammatical and (b) given that it is grammatical, show how the words are combined into phrases and how the phrases are put together to form larger phrases (including sentences). So, for example, a parser would use the rules we gave above to check that the sentence *The temperature has affected the printer* consists of a noun phrase, consisting of the noun *Temperature* followed by an auxiliary verb, followed by a verb phrase, and that the verb phrase *affected the printer* consists of the verb *affect* and a noun phrase consisting of the noun *printers*. In effect, this gives the same information as the sorts of tree structure we have given above, for example in Figure 3.5. Thus, one can think of a parser as taking sentences, and producing such representations (assuming the sentences are in fact well-formed according to the grammar).

How can this be done? There are many ways to apply the rules to the input to produce an output tree – many different **procedures**, or **parsing algorithms** by which an input string can be assigned a structure. Here is one method:

1 For each word in the sentence, find a rule whose right hand side matches it. This means that every word would then be labelled with its part of speech (shown on the left hand side of the rule that matched it). This step is exactly equivalent to looking up the words in an English dictionary. Given rules of the type N → user, N → printer, and V → clean, this will produce a partial structure as we can see at the top left corner (Stage 0) of Figure 3.7.

2 Starting from the left hand end of the sentence, find every rule whose right-hand side will match one or more of the parts of speech (Stage 1 of Figure 3.7).

3 Keep on doing step 2, matching larger and larger bits of phrase structure until no more rules can be applied. (In our example, this will be when the sentence rule finally matches up with a noun phrase and a verb phrase which have already been identified). The sentence is now parsed (Stage 2-4 of Figure 3.7).

It is generally possible to find more than one algorithm to produce a given result. As already mentioned, this is certainly true of parsing: the algorithm given here is just one of many possible variants which differ in their ability to cope efficiently with different types of grammar. The one we gave started out with the words of the sentence, and built the tree 'bottom up'. However, we could also have used an algorithm that built the tree 'top-down', starting with the S node. Essentially, what this algorithm would do is guess that it is looking at a sentence, and then guess that the sentence starts with a noun phrase, and then guess that the noun phrase consists of a noun, and then check to see whether there really is a noun at the start of the sentence. Each time there is a choice of possibilities (maybe the noun phrase starts with a determiner) it makes the first choice and, if that proves incorrect, backs up and tries the next alternative. During the course of parsing a sentence with a complicated grammar it would eventually get the right answer – perhaps only after many wrong guesses. (The algorithms that MT and other NLP systems use are more sophisticated and efficient than this, of course). The first few stages in a top-down parse are illustrated in Figure 3.8.

This description applies only to building the surface, constituent structure tree, of course. As regards other levels of representation (representations of grammatical relations, and semantic representations), there are two basic approaches, as we noted above. If information about other levels of representation is represented as annotations on the constituent structure rules, then it should be possible to construct these other representations at the same time as the constituent structure representation. This is slightly harder if the relationships between levels is stated in a separate collection of rules. In this case, the natural thing to do is to first build the

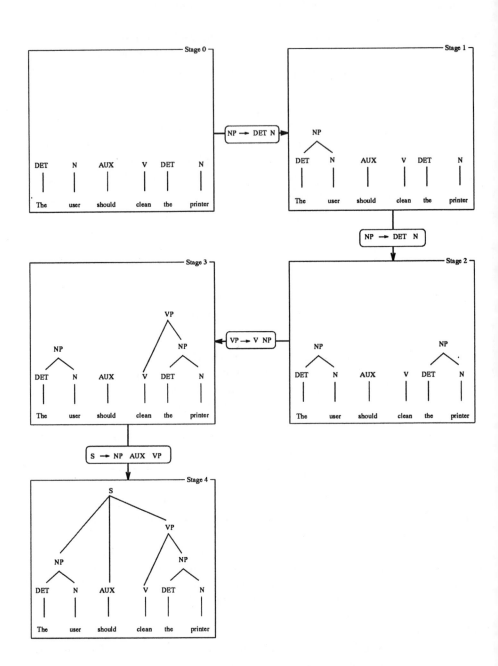

Figure 3.7 Parsing Using a Bottom-Up Algorithm

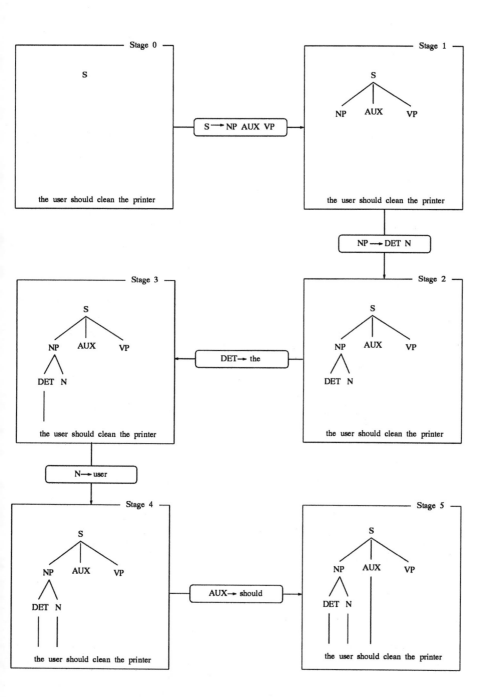

Figure 3.8 Parsing Using a Top-Down Algorithm

constituent structure representation, and apply these rules to that representation.

The simplest procedure for this operates 'recursively' down the surface (constituent) structure tree, dealing with each node in turn. Beginning at the root node, the algorithm looks for a rule whose lhs matches this node, and its daughters. In the case of the following rule (which we gave above, but repeat here for convenience), this means the root node must be labelled with an S, and there must be three daughters, labelled NP, AUX, and VP, and the VP must in turn contain a daughter labelled V, and a daughter labelled NP.

[$_S$ NP:$1, AUX:$2, [$_{VP}$ V:$3, NP:$4]]
↔
[$_S$ HEAD:$3, SUBJECT:$1, OBJECT:$4]

One interpretation of such a rule leaves the constituent structure tree untouched, and creates a new structure representing the grammatical relations. This requires the algorithm to create a temporary structure corresponding to the rhs of the rule. This will be labelled S, and will contain three daughters, one the HEAD, one the SUBJECT, and one the OBJECT. Of course, this structure cannot be complete yet, because it is not yet known what these daughters should contain. However, the algorithm now deals with the daughter nodes of the surface structure tree in exactly the same way as it dealt with the root node (hence the process is called recursive). That is, it tries to find rules to match each of NP, AUX, V, and NP, and produce the corresponding structures. When it has done this, it will be able to fill in the parts of the temporary structure it created originally, and a representation of the grammatical relations will have been produced. This can be seen in Figure 3.9.

A similar procedure can be used to interpret the rules that relate grammatical relation structures to semantic structures. There are a number of details and refinements which should really be described, such as how we ensure that all possible grammatical relation structures are produced, what we do about nodes that are mentioned on the LHS but not on the RHS, and so on. But these are refinements, and do not matter here, so long as this basic picture is clear.

3.3.2   Generation

So far, we have described how to take an input string, and produce a representation. But, obviously, for most applications, the reverse process is also necessary. Equally obviously, how hard this is depends on where you start from. Generating a string from a constituent structure representation like those above is almost trivial. At worst one needs to do something to the words to get the correct form (e.g. to get *clean*, not *cleans* in *The user should clean the printer regularly*). For the rest, it is simply a matter of 'forgetting' what structure there is (and perhaps the not-so-trivial matter of arranging punctuation).

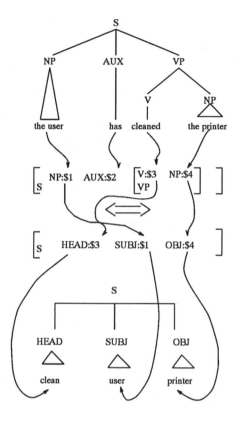

Figure 3.9 Building a Representation of Grammatical Relations

Starting from a representation of grammatical relations, or a semantic representation is harder.

If the relations between syntactic, grammatical relation structures, and semantic structures are described by means of explicit rules, then one approach is to use those rules in the same way as we described for parsing, but 'in reverse' — that is with the part of the rule written after the ⟷ interpreted as the lhs. Things are not quite so straightforward when information about grammatical relations, and/or semantics is packed into the constituent structure rules.

One possibility is to have a completely separate set of procedures for producing sentences from semantic or grammatical relation structures, without going through the constituent structure stage (for example, one would need a rule that puts HEAD, SUBJECT, and OBJECT into the normal word order for English, depending on whether the sentence was active or passive, interrogative or declarative). This has attractions, in particular, it may be that one does not want to be able to generate exactly the sentences one can parse (one may want one's parser to accept stylistically rather bad sentences, which one would not want to produce, for example). However, the disadvantage is that one will end up describing again most, if not all, of the knowledge that is contained in the grammar which is used for parsing.

A naive (and utterly impractical) approach would be to simply apply constituent structure rules at random, until a structure was produced that matched the grammatical relation structure that is input to generation. A useful variation of this is to start with the whole input structure, and take all the rules for the category S (assuming one expects the structure to represent a sentence), and to compare the grammatical relation structure each of these rules produces with the input structure. If the structure produced by a particular rule matches the input structure, then build a partial tree with this rule, and mark each of these parts as belonging to that tree. For example, given the rule for S above, one could take the grammatical relation structure of a sentence like *The user has cleaned the printer* and begin to make a phrase structure tree, as is illustrated in Figure 3.10.

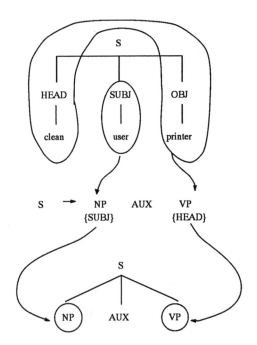

Figure 3.10   Generation from a Grammatical Relation Structure 1

One can see that a partial constituent structure tree has been created, whose nodes are linked to parts of the grammatical relation structure (a convention is assumed here whereby everything not explicitly mentioned in the rule is associated with the HEAD element). Now all that is necessary is to do the same thing to all the parts of the Grammatical relation structure, attaching the partial trees that have been constructed in the appropriate places. This is illustrated in Figure 3.11. Again, there are many refinements and details missed out here, but again, all that matters is the basic picture.

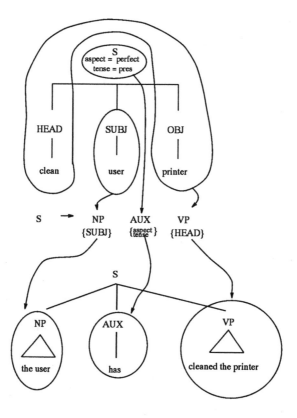

Figure 3.11 Generation from a Grammatical Relation Structure 2

3.4 Summary

This chapter has introduced the different kinds of knowledge needed to do translation, namely grammatical or syntactic knowledge, semantic, pragmatic and real world knowledge. Focussing on syntactic and semantic knowledge, we then looked at how this knowledge can be represented and described. Finally, again concentrating on syntax and semantics, we looked briefly at how this knowledge can be used for processing by means of parsing and generation algorithms.

3.5 Further Reading

A somewhat more detailed discussion of many of the issues touched on in this Chapter can be found in [Hutchins and Somers, 1992], especially Chapters 1, 3, 5, and 7.

The issue of how linguistic knowledge should be represented and described is one of the key concerns of Linguistic theory, and will be covered by most introductory books on Linguistics. On syntax, [Brown and Miller, 1991] is an accessible introduction. An elementary introduction to linguistic semantics can be found in [Hurford and Heasley, 1983], a somewhat more advanced introduction can be found in [Kempson, 1977].

It is by no means the case that linguists agree on the sorts of representation that are required, though the use of some kind of constituent structure is almost universal. In particular, there is disagreement about how one should think about more abstract levels of representation. Here [Borsley, 1991] provides a useful comparative discussion at an introductory level. Discussion of the special requirements that MT makes of linguistic representation and description can be found in [Van Eynde, 1993b].

The issue of how linguistic representations and descriptions can be used for processing is the topic of the fields of Computational Linguistics and Natural Language Processing (NLP). Here [Allen, 1987; Grishman, 1986; Gazdar and Mellish, 1989] and [Winograd, 1983] provide excellent introductions, though all go well beyond what is required for a basic understanding. Parts of [Charniak and Wilks, 1976] are more elementary, though now somewhat out of date.

Much work in NLP focusses on analysis rather than synthesis or generation. For an introduction to issues in generation, see [McDonald, 1987].

NLP is also a key area of interest in the field of Artificial Intelligence (AI), and many introductions to AI contain some useful introductory material on NLP, examples are [Rich, 1983; Charniak and McDermott, 1985; Tennant, 1981; Barr and Fiegenbaum, 1981]. Many of the entries in [Shapiro, 1987] will also be useful.

Chapter 4

Machine Translation Engines

4.1 Introduction

In Chapter 2, we gave an overview of the environment in which a typical MT system might operate, and outlined the various processes and parts involved. In Chapter 3, we discussed how basic linguistic knowledge can be represented and used for automatic analysis and synthesis. It is now time to look inside the most important non-human component in MT — the component that actually performs automatic translation — what we will call the **translation engine**.

MT engines can be classified by their architecture — the overall processing organisation, or the abstract arrangement of its various processing modules. Traditionally, MT has been based on **direct** or **transformer** architecture engines, and this is still the architecture found in many of the more well-established commercial MT systems. We shall therefore look at this architecture in detail in Section 4.2 before moving on to consider the newer **indirect** or **linguistic knowledge** architectures which, having dominated MT research for several years, are starting to become available in commercial form (Section 4.3).

4.2 Transformer Architectures

The main idea behind transformer engines is that input (source language) sentences can be transformed into output (target language) sentences by carrying out the simplest possible parse, replacing source words with their target language equivalents as specified in a bilingual dictionary, and then roughly re-arranging their order to suit the rules of the target language. The overall arrangement of such an Engine is shown in Figure 4.1.

The first stage of processing involves the parser, which does some preliminary analysis of the source sentence. The result need not be a complete representation of the kind described in Chapter 3, but might just be a list of words with their parts of speech. This is passed to a package of rules which transform the sentence into a target sentence, using — where necessary — information provided by the parsing process. The transformation rules include bilingual dictionary rules and various rules to re-order words. They may also include rules to change the form of target words, for example, to make sure verbs have the correct person, number, and tense suffixes.

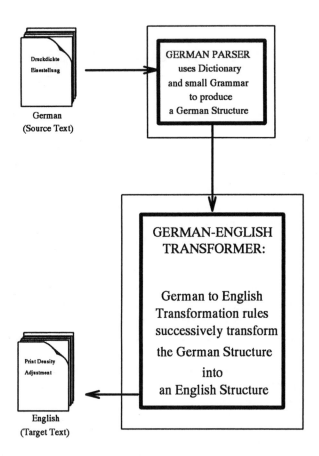

Figure 4.1 A Transformer Architecture (German to English)

To get a more detailed idea of how it works, we shall examine the steps in the translation of a sentence taken from the printer manual text in Chapter 2:

(1)   Drehen Sie den Knopf eine Position zurück. 'Turn you the button one position back.' (Turn the button back one position.)

Step 1: The German words are looked up in a German electronic dictionary, and the appropriate category (for example, noun, verb) is assigned. In this particular case the look-up is easy: almost all the words in the sentence are present in their base form — the form they normally have as dictionary entries. The only exceptions to this are the determiners *den* and *eine*, which are inflected forms of *der* and *ein* and have to be recognised as such. After all, an electronic dictionary is likely to be similar to an ordinary paper dictionary in that regularly inflected forms of verbs, nouns, adjectives and determiners are not given since they can be deduced from general rules. This is why most MT systems make use of a morphological component. This component contains specific rules that deal with the regularities of inflection. Take for example a verb like *drehen* ('turn'), which has the 3rd person singular form *dreht* ('turns'). This form is not shown in monolingual or bilingual paper dictionaries like Düden because other verbs of the same general form have the same form for 3rd person singular. If the input sentence contained *dreht*, the lookup system would first follow its general policy of looking up directly. Assuming that fails, it would then refer to some built-in inflection rules to see if they could be used to derive an infinitive or stem form. One rule might say (in effect) "If the word has *t* on the end, it might be a 3rd person singular verb. Try to confirm the hypothesis by removing the *t*, adding infinitive/imperative *en*, then looking for the resultant *drehen*." A detailed account of the type of rules that we can encounter in a morphological component is described in Chapter 5.

Note that the generalizations of a morphological component can also help the system to deal with words which are not in its dictionary in any form at all. In the past few years, German has acquired the verbs *faxen* and *mailen*, which are derived from English *to fax* and *to (electronically) mail*. Let us suppose they are not in the German dictionary. If *mailt* or *faxt* are encountered in the input, our 3rd person singular rule could apply and, as a result of the verb annotation on the RHS, it would 'guess' that the input forms might be 3rd person singular versions of the hypothesised verb *mailen* or *faxen*. Obviously this hypothesis cannot be confirmed in the available dictionary, but it is certainly useful: the parser can now work on the assumption that the unknown word is probably a verb — this is much more helpful in the parse process than having no idea at all what its category/part of speech might be.

One problem with which the system also has to deal is the fact that the two words *drehen* and *zurück* together form the main verb of the sentence: *zurückdrehen*. The recognition may be done by a rule which specifies that prepositions which stand alone (i.e. without a complement) at the end of a sentence can form part of the main verb. This possibility is then checked in the dictionary, which should contain an entry for the verb *zurückdrehen*.

Step 2: Some rules of a German grammar are used to try to parse the sentence. This parse might result in the assumption that the NP *den Knopf* ('the button') is the object of *zurückdrehen* and (possibly) that the next NP *eine Position* is a modifier of some sort. An advanced parser might work out that it is in fact a *measure* modifier. However, it is quite possible that the transformer Engine will not need any parse at all in this case (beyond identification of the category of the words in the string). This is because the difference between the German and some possible English translations is not great.

Step 3: The Engine now applies some German to English transformation rules. The first step here is to find translations of the German words in a German to English dictionary. Taking the simple cases, *der* — the nominative form of *den* — goes to *the*, *Knopf* goes to *button*, *ein* to *a*, *Position* to *position*. The rules might have the following form:

> *knopf*{cat=n} → *button*{cat=n}
>
> *ein*{cat=det} → *a*{cat=det}
>
> . . .
>
> . . .

and so on. That is, when *knopf* is a noun (cat=n) it is translated as *button*. Similarly, *ein* translates as the determiner *a* — in the present context, *ein* would be best translated as *one*, but let us assume that it is routinely translated as *a* by the Engine.

Turning to *zurückdrehen*, there needs to be a rule which says "If there is an imperative verb X, followed by the NP *Sie*, the translation is the translation of X. In this case, we have an imperative verb (*zurückdrehen*) followed by the NP *Sie*, so we will get *turn back* as the translation. This rule is intended to prevent the translation of the German NP *Sie* which functions as the subject. English imperatives do not have an overt subject and therefore the literal translation *Turn back you the button one position* is unacceptable. Our proposed rule would give *Turn back the button a position*, which is better[1].

In practice, the imperative translation might be handled by a pair of rules. The first could look like this:

> X{cat=v,mood=imperative} *Sie*
> →
> X

The LHS matches cases where there is any imperative verb X followed by *Sie*. The RHS says that the translation of such a structure simply consists of the translation of the imperative verb.

As we have stated it, this first rule has not done any translation. What it has done

---

[1] Another possibility would be to have another rule which put the translated preposition immediately after the verb object, giving *Turn the button back a position*.

is to re-order part of the German sentence prior to translation into English. The Engine can now simply apply the lexical translation rules to the re-ordered sentence:

zurückdrehen → turn_back

After applying all these rules, the Engine now has an internal representation of the form *Turn back the button a position.*

Step 4: The Engine would now apply rules which turn the stem or dictionary forms of English words to their inflected forms. As it happens, in the present example, the English stem forms happen to be exactly what is wanted. For example, the stem form *turn* which the dictionary supplied is identical to imperative *turn*. Moreover, all the nouns are singular, so it is unnecessary to add any plural affixes (e.g. *s* or *es*).

This discussion is rather sketchy and we have ignored many details. For example, we have said very little about how the various types of transformation rule should be ordered: how should re-ordering rules be interleaved with the bilingual dictionary rules? We have also not said anything much here about how the system copes with ambiguities, or how rules are prevented from applying in the wrong circumstances; for example, it will not always be the case that a preposition at the end of a German clause 'belongs' to an earlier imperative verb. However, this should have given the reader an impression of what is involved in a transformer architecture. We can now summarize some of the distinctive design features of this sort of engine:

- Input sentences are automatically parsed only so far as it is necessary for the successful operation of the various lexical (word-based) and phrasal transformation rules. The transformer engine is often content to find out just a few incomplete pieces of information about the structure of some of the phrases in a sentence, and where the main verb might be, rather than worrying about getting a full and complete parse for the whole thing. In other words, parsing may stop before an S rule of the kind described in Chapter 3 has been applied.

  In practice, transformer systems tend not to have particularly large grammars for the language they translate from. Thus in the German to English transformer system discussed above, we assumed that the grammar covered only some features of German. As a consequence it would not be able to decide for many (or perhaps any) input sentences whether it is grammatically acceptable.

- The use of limited grammars and incomplete parsing means that transformer systems do not generally construct elaborate representations of input sentences — in many cases, not even the simplest surface constituent structure tree. As we will see, other types of MT system construct much more abstract and deep representations.

- Most of the engine's translational competence lies in the rules which transform bits of input sentence into bits of output sentence, including the bilingual dictionary rules. In a sense a transformer system has some knowledge of the **comparative grammar** of the two languages — of what makes the one structurally different from the other.

- Inflection rules aside, transformers generally have no independent linguistic knowledge of the target language because they have no independent grammar for that language. In the German-English system, there would be few, if any, independently stated rules about English — although you could perhaps infer some aspects of English grammar from the rules which transform bits of German into bits of 'English'.

Given these general features, we can describe the translational behaviour that can be expected from a system with a transformer engine.

Characteristic to the performance of such a system is the fact that the engine will not be particularly troubled when faced with unusual, marginally acceptable or frankly unacceptable source language sentences; it will rarely have sufficient source language grammatical knowledge to recognise something as ungrammatical. If the grammatical structures in the input sentence are not recognised by some transforming rule, that structure will pass through to the output sentence without any re-arrangement. We have seen this in the example above, where all the word order and structure of *Drehen Sie den Knopf eine Position zurück* apart from the relationship between *drehen* and *zurück* was passed through into the English output. Something similar is true for the words in the input sentence: if they are not found in the system's dictionary then they are passed through into the English output and remain untranslated. As a consequence of these features this type of architecture implies that, in the worst case, the whole input sentence could survive unchanged as the output sentence. This would happen in the highly unlikely case that none of the input words are found in the bilingual dictionary and none of the input sentence grammatical structure is recognised.

With regard to the target language performance of the system we can say that since the system has no detailed knowledge of target language grammar there is no guarantee that the transformed input sentence is actually a grammatical sentence in the target language. Although in most cases output will resemble the target language (especially the use of target language words), the result can sometimes be a completely unintelligible 'word salad'. In such cases one could say that the output does not belong to any known language — natural or artificial.

The typical design features of a transformer system pose some restrictions on the development of additional language modules. First, the engine will run in one direction only, for example, from German to English. If the engine developer wants it to go in the other direction she more or less has to completely rewrite the transformer rules. Since the transformer rules include bilingual dictionary rules, this can mean that the Engine has to be supplied with two bilingual dictionaries, for example,

German-English and English-German. This is rather clumsy since, apart from the differences in their directionality, the dictionaries contain much the same information. Secondly, the engine links a single pair of languages only. If the developer wants it to translate into another target language then again she more or less has to completely re-write the transformer rules. Again, this amounts to rewriting most of the system. Grammatical knowledge of English and of German which is built into a German-English system cannot then be transferred to a English-French or a German-French system. Even in cases where a system contains only a rather limited grammatical knowledge of the languages it involves reproducing this knowledge for the development of other language pairs means an unnecessary time loss.

Drawing these various points together, we can summarise the situation of the transformer engine architecture as follows:

- It is highly **robust**. That is, the Engine does not break down or stop in an 'error condition' when it encounters input which contains unknown words or unknown grammatical constructions. Robustness is clearly important for general-purpose MT.

- In the worst case it can work rather badly, being prone to produce output that is simply unacceptable in the target language ('word salad').

- The translation process involves many different rules interacting in many different ways. This makes transformer systems rather hard to understand in practice — which means that they can be hard to extend or modify.

- The transformer approach is really designed with translation in one direction, between one pair of languages in mind, it is not conducive to the development of genuinely multi-lingual systems (as opposed to mere collections of independent one-pair, one-direction engines).

To close this section, we give an example of a German Teletext Travel News broadcast and a translation produced by an actual small transformer Engine (which is available commercially, and rather cheaply for use on PCs). The source text and the raw (unedited) MT output are given on page 70. The Engine is clearly struggling here with unfamiliar words and structures, occasionally producing completely unintelligible output which would be unsuitable even for gisting. This example represents the 'bottom end' of transformer performance, but gives a good idea of how useful even this quality of translation can be — readers with no knowledge of German will certainly get more information from the translation than they could from the original. Note, however, that the quality of the output could be improved considerably if the system were adapted to dealing with this particular text type and vocabulary. As we mentioned in Chapter 2, tuning the system to a particular text type is worthwhile if the input consists of many texts of that type.

Source Text

VEREINZELT BADEVERBOT

Sommerurlauber an den Küsten Südeuropas oder der Ost- und Nordsee müssen vereinzelt mit Beeinträchtigungen des Badespaßes rechnen.

An der Adria wird bei Eraclea Mare und Caorle wegen bakterieller Belastungen vom Baden abgeraten.

An der Cote d'Azur ist laut ADAC vereinzelt mit Verschmutzungen durch Teer und Öl zu rechnen.

Auch in Spanien werde an einigen Stellen bei Barcelona vom Baden abgeraten.

Zufriedenstellend lautet die Wertung für die Nordsee in Schleswig-Holstein und den Niederlanden.

Zugleich treten aber in der Nordsee vereinzelt tennisballgroße Phenolklumpen auf.

Unedited Output

ISOLATED BADEVERBOT

Summer vacationers at the coasts of South Europe or the east - and North Sea must calculate isolated with impairments of the bath joke.

At the Adria Mare and Caorle is dissuaded at Eraclea because of bacterial burdens from the bath.

At the Code D'Azur is to be calculated loudly ADAC isolated with pollutions through tar and oil. Also in Spain am dissuaded at some places at Barcelona from the bath.

Satisfactorily the appraisal sounds for the North Sea in Schleswig-Holstein and the Netherlands. At the same time tennisballegrosse appear however in the North Sea isolated Phenolklumpen.

4.3   Linguistic Knowledge Architectures

The second major architecture — **indirect** or **linguistic knowledge** (LK) architecture — has dominated research in MT design during the past decade and is starting to appear in a number of commercial systems. The idea behind LK engines is straightforward enough:

> High quality MT requires linguistic knowledge of *both* the source and the target languages as well as the differences between them.

We use the term 'linguistic knowledge' to refer to extensive formal grammars which permit abstract/relatively deep analyses in the sense of Chapter 3. We shall see later on just how deep the analysis can go.

With the Transformer architecture, the translation process relies on some knowledge of the source language and some knowledge about how to transform partly analysed source sentences into strings that look like target language sentences. With the LK architecture, on the other hand, translation relies on extensive knowledge of both the source *and* the target languages and of the relationships between analysed sentences in both languages. In short, LK architecture typically accords the target language the same status as the source language. As can be seen from Figure 4.2, the LK architecture requires two things:

- A substantial grammar of both the source language and the target language. These grammars are used by parsers to analyse sentences in each language into representations which show their underlying structure, and by generators to produce output sentences from such representations.

- An additional comparative grammar which is used to relate every source sentence representation to some corresponding target language representation — a representation which will form the basis for generating a target language translation.

The LK engine will have grammars for each language it deals with: in a German-English system, there would be one for German and one for English. Each of these grammars is an independent entity, i.e. there will be a set of rules which is identifiably for German, and another, separate set which is identifiably for English. In fact the physical and conceptual separation between the two grammars is such that in the initial stages of developing an LK engine, a group of English specialists might write the grammar for English entirely independently of another group of German specialists who are writing the system's German grammar. In such case both groups would have to aim though at a similar deep representation of their language, otherwise structural discrepancies can be created that would require extra transfer rules for mapping these different structures onto each other.

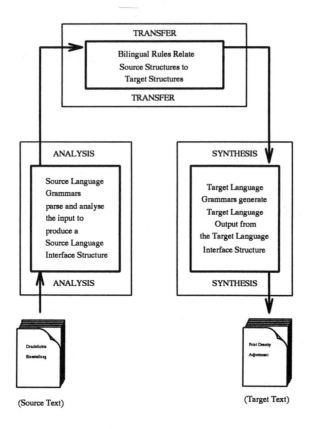

Figure 4.2 The Components of a Transfer System

Looking at Figure 4.2, it is clear that if (say) the system is translating from German to English, the first (analysis) step involves using the parser and the German grammar to analyse the German input. The second (transfer) step involves changing the underlying representation of the German sentence into an underlying representation of an English sentence. The third (synthesis) step and final major step involves changing the underlying English representation into an English sentence, using a generator and the English grammar. The fact that a proper English grammar is being used means that the output of the system — the English sentences — are far more likely to be grammatically correct than those of a German-English Transformer system (recall that the latter had no explicit English grammar to guide it). In fact, if (*per impossibile*) we had an LK German-English system with a 'perfect' English grammar the only sort of mistake it could make in the output would be errors in translational accuracy. That is, it would always produce perfectly well-formed English sentences even when it did not produce correct translations.

This also means that the whole Engine should be reversible, at least in theory. Taking the German-English LK engine in Figure 4.2, we could run the translation from right to left. That is, we could give it English sentences, which would then be analysed into underlying representations. These representations would be changed into German underlying representations and a German translation would then be synthesised from the result. The same grammars for each language are used regardless of the direction of the translation. In practice few translation engines are reversible, since some rules that are necessary for correct translation in one direction could cause problems if the process was reversed. This is especially true for lexical transfer rules, as we will see later on in this chapter.

With this general picture in mind, the next subsection focusses on the so-called transfer component, which embodies the comparative grammar that links the analysis and synthesis components together — the module in the centre of Figure 4.2.

4.3.1 Comparative Grammar and Transfer

We have said that parsers in LK engines typically analyse to relatively abstract, or deep underlying representations. Of course individual systems differ radically in the precise sorts of representations they use, but suppose the Engine uses the English grammar to produce the sort of deep syntactic representation we described in Chapter 3 (this is far from being the most abstract representation one can imagine, of course). If we are translating sentence (2) into German, the analysis component might produce a representation along the lines of Figure 4.3.

(2)   The temperature has affected the print density.

We can look at how the comparative grammar relates such a representation to corresponding representations for target language sentences. Just as each monolingual grammar has a 'dictionary' of rules (e.g. N → temperature) so also the comparative grammar has bilingual dictionary rules. In the simplest case, these may just relate source lexical items ('words') to target lexical items:

temperature ↔ temperatur

print_density ↔ druckdichte

affect ↔ beeinfluβen

One difference between these bilingual dictionary rules and those shown for the Transformer engine is that the latter were intended to be used in one direction only. The ↔ in the present rules indicates that they can (in principle) serve as English-German or German-English rules.

These dictionary rules can be seen as relating leaves (the word nodes) on the source language tree to leaves on the target language tree. The comparative grammar also contains some structural rules which relate other parts and nodes of the two trees to each other.

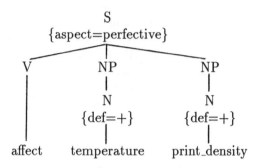

Figure 4.3   Abstract Tree Representation

One such structural rule might be read as follows: "The translation of the whole sentence is normally made up of the translation of the verb + the translation of the subject + the translation of the object." Note that 'translation' in this context has the restricted sense of translation into the corresponding target language representation — this representation has to be input to synthesis before a 'full' translation is reached. The structural rule we need might be written in the following way (where the LHS describes an English structure and the RHS describes the German, and $H, $S, and $O are variables interpreted as standing for pieces of English structure on one side, and for their translations on the other side).

[_S HEAD:$HEAD, D-SUBJ:$SUBJECT, D-OBJ:$OBJECT]
↔
[_S HEAD:$H, D-SUBJ:$S, D-OBJ:$O]

The left and right hand sides of the rule reflect the 'canonical' order (HEAD, then DEEP SUBJECT, then DEEP OBJECT) that one finds in the source (and target) representations. In some systems, the rule application procedure might be set up so that rule would work regardless of the left-right order of the nodes in the source representation.

This rule says that in the translation of the sentence as a whole, the HEAD is whatever the HEAD in the source language translates as. The HEAD is the verb *affect*, and its translation is given by a bilingual dictionary rule. The DEEP SUBJECT and DEEP OBJECT just contain single content words (*temperature* and *print_density*) and so they too are translated by the appropriate dictionary rules.

The annotations on the nodes of the representations must also be translated in some way. The rules relevant to our example are straightforward, indicating that the given values are simply carried over from source structure to target structure:

{def=+} ↔ {def=+}

{aspect=perfective} ↔ {aspect=perfective}

Of course, one could imagine that this 'copying' of information without changes could occur by default, i.e. features are copied unless a rule explicitly says otherwise (although specifying how this sort of system should actually work turns out to be surprisingly difficult).

Applying these rules to the English representation in Figure 4.3 will result in the construction of the corresponding German representation in Figure 4.4.

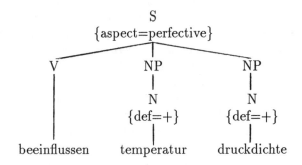

Figure 4.4 Tree Representation after Translation

This representation serves as input for the German synthesis module, which applies the rules of the German grammar to produce a German sentence. These rules will include one or more which require that the past participle of a verb is realised at the end of the clause when there is an auxiliary (*hat*, in this example). Thus, (3) should be produced as the translation.

(3)   Die Temperatur hat die Druckdichte beeinflußt

It should be clear that LK and Transformer architectures handle the word order problem rather differently. A Transformer engine generally preserves the surface order of the source language and directly re-uses it — with modifications where appropriate — to order the target language words. An LK engine, on the other hand, extracts all the information it can from the source word order and recodes this information in a more or less abstract representation. The generator for the target language will use the information in the representation and in the target language grammar to construct a target language sentence with a word order that it is grammatically appropriate for that language. In short, ordering information is not normally carried over directly.

The only differences between the English and the German representation in this example is in the words on the leaf nodes; the geometry and annotations on the tree are the same. Ideally, this similarity will hold for most sentences, so that most of the work in constructing the representation is done by the dictionary rules. However, it is important to realise that the design of the comparative grammar anticipates the possibility that the structures *could* be very different indeed if the differences between the source and its target language translation are very great. We will look at some such examples in the following chapters (cf. especially Chapter 6).

The similarity of the representations is related to the simplicity of the rules. For example, according to the rule, DEEP SUBJECTS translate as DEEP SUBJECTS, and DEEP OBJECTS as DEEP OBJECTS, and the rules for translating the words are stated without any conditions. But in general, one would only want to say that subjects and objects are *normally* translated as subjects and objects, and it is easy to think of cases where one would want to put extra conditions on such lexical rules. For example, English *import* translates as French *importer* when it is a verb, and *importation* when it is a noun, and the verb *effect* translates *réaliser* or *effet*, depending on whether it is a noun or a verb. Such examples can be multiplied at will. Similarly, one cannot always simply preserve the values of features such as **det**, or **aspect**. For example, in translating from English to French, one cannot generally expect to preserve the values of attributes indicating tense and aspect, if these are direct encodings of surface word forms (cf. Chapter 7).

A relatively straightforward example where a more complex rule is called for involves the translation of the English verb *like* into French *plaire*, as in (4), which shows the 'switching' of arguments.

(4)   a.   Sam likes the new laser printer.
      b.   La nouvelle imprimante à laser plaît à Sam.

Such a rule might look as follows:

[$_S$ HEAD:like, SUBJ:$1, OBJ:$2]
↔
[$_S$ HEAD:plaire, SUBJ:$2, OBJ:$1]

Switching of arguments occurs because the variables $1, and $2 are associated with different grammatical relations on the two sides of the rule ($1 will be bound to the representation of *Sam*, and $2 will be bound to the representation of *the new laser printer* (on the English side of the rule), and *la nouvelle imprimante à laser* (on the French side of the rule)). The identity of the words that fill the HEAD relation has been given to prevent this rule applying to examples involving 'normal' verbs (one will also have to make sure that the 'normal' rules do not apply in translating *like* and *plaire*, of course). This process of argument switching is illustrated in Figure 4.5.

Special rules like the one given above have to be written for *every* case where there is some difference between the output of the source language analysis and the input expected by the target language generator. In practice, one would expect the contrastive grammar for an English-French, or English-German MT system whose most abstract representations involve surface grammatical relations to be quite large.

In general, the size and complexity of a comparative grammar can be reduced by increasing the depth of the parsing towards more abstract levels of representation. For example, the use of *Semantic Relations* (see Chapter 3) would remove the need for a special *like-plaire* rule, because both English and French sentences in (4) would have representations with *Sam* as EXPERIENCER, and *the new laser printer/la nouvelle imprimante à laser* as THEME.[2]

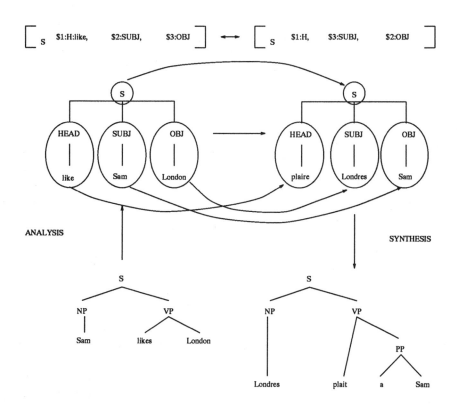

Figure 4.5 Complex Transfer

The discussion so far may give the impression that there is a single transfer approach to MT. But this is far from being the case. For one thing, different systems use different styles, and levels of representation. For another thing, we have only given

---

[2]The names of these particular Semantic Relations should not be taken too seriously. In fact, of course, it does not much matter *what* the relations are called, so long as they are the same in the source and target grammars.

one view of the relation of the various components. That other views are possible is indicated below, where we discuss some variable aspects of transfer systems.

Intermediate representations in transfer As we have described transfer, the mapping between source and target structure is direct in the sense that there are no intermediate structures. There are, for example, no structures which have target words, and source geometry. Some systems, however, make a distinction between lexical transfer (which simply changes source words to target words) and structural transfer (where rules actually change the shape of the tree) with one set of rules being applied before the other. Also, the rules we have given each deal with a structure in one step, without using an intermediate representation. But it is possible to have a transfer rule which changes the source tree in some way, producing an intermediate representation, that must have another rule applied to it before a genuine target structure results. The problem with systems that allow this is that problems of complex rule interaction can occur, in the way that they do with a transformer architecture. We have allowed for a limited degree of collaboration between rules that deal with structure, and rules that deal with features, for example. The advantage of this is that we do not have to state facts about the relation between, for example, determination values in each rule. This seems both natural and economical in terms of effort involved. The disadvantage of this is that it increases the number of rules that must be applied in order to translate each tree. An alternative is to state the rules separately like this, but in some way compiling them together, to produce rules that deal with entire subtrees. The problem with this is that the set of compiled rules tends to be very large.

Symmetry Throughout this chapter the picture of transfer that we have described is rather **symmetric**. That is, it assumes the target structure is rather similar to the source structure in the sense of being of corresponding depth of analysis or linguistic abstraction. This suggests analysis and synthesis are to a large extent 'inverses' of each other. But this is not a requirement. It is possible to imagine systems where the input to transfer was a deep syntactic representation, and the output was a representation of surface syntactic structure. Moreover, in a one-directional system for one pair of languages, no real distinction might be drawn between transfer and synthesis. Symmetry is however desirable as soon as one deals with more than one language or direction. In such cases the advantages become obvious, having a separate synthesis component with a role broadly the inverse of to that of analysis — not only can the same synthesis component be used for all transfer pairs, but one will avoid duplicating work by using the same (or similar) grammars in analysis and synthesis.

Reversibility We noted that transfer rules could be reversible *in principle*, and though this is natural, and attractive (because it halves the number of transfer components one has to construct and makes testing easier, since, if a rule works in one direction it should work in the other), it is not obvious that reversible transfer rules are always possible, or desirable. This is because a system should be able to translate a wide variety of input strings, some of them the type of string that one would normally not want to produce as output. As a simple lexical example of the reversibility problem consider the slightly old-fashioned Dutch word *aanvangen*. One would like to be able to translate this into English as *begin*, but one would normally not want to translate *begin* into *aanvangen*. One would choose the more common verb *beginnen* instead. So the following translation rule cannot be reversible:

```
aanvangen → begin
```

Well-formedness In order for transfer output to be useful for synthesis it is desirable that it is in some sense well-formed for the target language. To produce well-formed target language structures transfer components can become rather complex. Some systems supplement normal transfer with a set of adjustment rules which transform the output of transfer to make it more suitable for input to the target synthesis.

Instructions for synthesis The target structure that is produced by transfer has been described as a simple linguistic tree — it does not contain, for example, special instructions to guide synthesis. Some systems do contain this sort of information: transfer attaches what are essentially small programs to nodes of the target tree, which are executed in synthesis.

Choosing between possible translations In general, several different transfer rules will be able to apply to a structure, giving alternative (not necessarily correct) translations. The question arises as to how to choose between these. One crude possibility is to organize the rules so they apply in sequence, taking the results of the first rule that produces a 'correct' target structure (correct in the sense of getting an acceptable target sentence, perhaps). Alternatively, one could apply all these rules and find some way of scoring the results, so as to prefer the better ones. A complementary question which arises in the case where no translation rule applies (because none matches the source structure) is whether one should leave the structure untranslated (it may be, for example, a proper name), or to try to force a rule to apply?

Declarative or procedural processing If the answer to the problem above is to organize the rules so they apply in sequence then the result is the contamination of **declarative** information in the comparative grammar with **procedural** information – information about the order in which things should be done. This violates a widely accepted principle that it should be possible to describe the relevant linguistic facts in an MT system independently of the ways the engine actually uses them. The advantages of a declarative system are (a) ease of understanding, modification and debugging, and (b) independence of particular implementations or algorithms: if a collection of rules is declarative, it will be possible to consider alternative algorithms for applying them, with some confidence that the same results will be produced, which allows one to find the most efficient way of processing. Despite these advantages of declarativity there is a strong temptation to introduce non-declarative characteristics (e.g. to ensure that the most likely transfer rules are tried early, and block the application of other rules, so cutting down the space of possibilities that have to be processed). Thus, though declarativity is a generally accepted goal, it is a property that systems have in different degrees, and it is not even generally agreed what the correct compromise between efficiency and declarativity is.

4.3.2   Interlinguas

The general idea suggested by the discussion of the *like-plaire* example at the end of the previous section is that comparative grammar (hence transfer) becomes simpler as linguistic analysis goes deeper — as the representations become more abstract. In fact, a major objective of MT research is to define a level of analysis which is so deep that the comparative grammar component disappears completely. Given such a level of representation, the output of analysis could be the direct input to the target synthesis component. Representations at such a level would have to capture whatever is common between sentences (and expressions of other categories) and their translations — that is they would have to be representations of 'meaning' (in some sense). Moreover, such a level of representation would have to be entirely language independent — for example, if it preserved features of the source language, one would still require a transfer component of some kind to produce the corresponding features of the target language. For this reason, such a level of representation is normally called an **Interlingua**, and systems that use such a level are called **Interlingual**.

The relationship between transfer and interlingual systems can be pictured as in Figure 4.6. As one can see, the size of the contrastive grammar (hence the transfer component) between two languages decreases as the level of representation becomes more abstract. As this diagram perhaps suggests, the difference between transfer representations and interlinguas is a matter of degree rather than absolute distinction (for example, Chapter 7 shows how one might combine an interlingual representation of tense and aspect with a transfer approach to other phenomena).

There are a number of clear attractions to an interlingual architecture. First, from a purely intellectual or scientific point of view, the idea of an interlingua is interesting, and exciting. Second, from a more practical point of view, an interlingual system promises to be much easier to extend by adding new language pairs, than a transfer system (or a transformer system). This is because, providing the interlingua is properly designed, it should be possible to add a new language to a system simply by adding analysis and synthesis components for it. Compare this with a transfer system, where one needs not only analysis and synthesis, but also transfer components into all the other languages involved in the system. Since there is one transfer for each language pair, N languages require $N \times N - 1$ transfer components (one does not need a transfer component from a language into itself). For example, extending a system for 3 languages into one for 5 means writing 14 new transfer components (as one goes from 6 to 20 transfer components), and going from a 5 language system to a 9 language system means going from 20 components to 72.

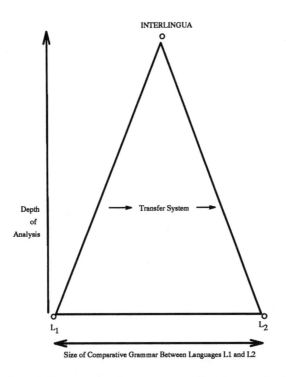

The size of the comparative grammar that is required to translate between two languages gets smaller as the 'depth' of the representations used increases. As the representations become more abstract, there are fewer differences between source and target representations and it is easier to relate them. Ultimately, a level of representation may be achieved where source and target representations are identical, where no comparative grammar is needed. In this situation, the representations which are produced by analysis could be directly input to the target language synthesis component. Such a level of representation is called an **interlingua**, and a system that uses such a level is called an **interlingual** system.

Figure 4.6 Transfer and Interlingua

Ideas about interlinguas are intimately tied up with ideas about the representation of meaning. We will look at this in more detail in Chapter 7. However, one can get a flavour of the problems that are involved in defining an interlingua by considering the following.

Producing an interlingual representation involves producing a representation that is entirely language independent (for the languages one wants to translate, at least).

This involves producing a language independent representation of words, and the structures they appear in. Under the latter heading, one would have to make sure one could represent the difference in meaning between examples like those in (5) — assuming one does not want them all to translate alike, that is — and find a way of representing the meaning that is expressed by various tenses, and by the distinction between definite, and indefinite NPs (e.g. *a printer* vs. *the printer*).

(5)   a.   It was the printer that was serviced yesterday.

   b.   It was yesterday that the printer was serviced.

   c.   The printer was serviced yesterday.

While this raises many unsolved linguistic problems, it is the language independent representation of word meaning that seems to pose the most difficult problems. The central problem is how to choose the vocabulary of the interlingua — what are the primitive concepts of the meaning representation to be. Notice that this is not a question of what *names* we should give the concepts — how we should write them down or represent them. Of course, we should make sure that we do not use one name for two concepts, which might be confusing, but beyond this, we can give them, for example, names from an existing language (e.g. English, or Esperanto), or numbers, or codes in some invented language — the only difference here will be how easy they are to write or remember. The problem is one of identity. For example, are we to include a concept that we might write as CORNER — this being the interlingual representation of the English noun *corner*? This seems natural enough from the point of view of English, but from the point of view of, for example, Spanish it is not so natural, because in Spanish there are different words for inside corners (*rincón*) and outside corners (*esquina*). Is there any reason why we should not choose a more specific primitive word for our representation, for example, OUTSIDE-CORNER and INSIDE-CORNER. Similar problems will arise wherever one language has several words that correspond to one word in another. The point is that different languages 'carve the world up' differently, so settling the choice of vocabulary for the interlingua will involve either (i) some apparently arbitrary decisions about which language's conceptualization to take as basic, or (ii) 'multiplying out' all the distinctions found in any language. In the latter case one will have two interlingual items for English *corner* (because of Spanish), two for English *river* (because of the distinction between *rivière* and *fleuve* in French), and two for English *eat*, because of the distinction between *essen* (for humans) and *fressen* (for animals) in German. When one consider more distant languages like Japanese, even more distinctions will arise — Japanese does not distinguish between wearing and putting on, as does English, but does make a distinction according to where the item is worn or put on (e.g. on the head vs on the hands). Of course, one solution to this multiplicity of concepts is to try to reduce the set of *primitive* concepts, defining complex concepts in terms of the primitive ones. For example, one might think that EAT is not a primitive, but that INGEST is, and that the interlingual representation of the meaning of *eat* should involve INGEST, and some other primitives. However, though this solves the problem of the number of concepts, it does not overcome the problem of arbitrariness, and it raises the problem of finding an adequate set of primitives to capture the relevant distinctions (the reader might, as an exercise, like to consider what a set of primitives would look like to distinguish a handful of verbs like *eat*, *drink*, *gobble up*, *feed on*, or find a set of primitives that will distinguish between different kinds of furniture (chairs, stools, tables, etc.)).

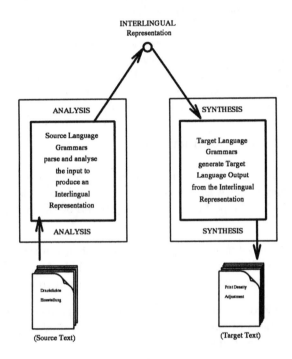

Figure 4.7 The Components of an Interlingual System

A further problem is that using an interlingua in MT can lead to extra, unnecessary work, in some cases. For example, suppose one has an interlingua intended for translation between English, French, and Japanese. Japanese distinguishes terms for older and younger brother and sister, and for various relatives depending on whether they belong to the speaker, or to the hearer (i.e. the term for *my mother* is different from that for *your mother*, or *mothers in general*). The problem is that this distinction has to be encoded in the interlingua, so one must decide if English *brother* is an older brother or a younger brother, even if one is not translating into Japanese. For example, translating *Sam's brother has already left* into French will involve dealing with an ambiguity, since there will be two interlingual representations differing as to whether the brother is older or younger than Sam. But of course, this is irrelevant for both English and French, and one can manage with a very simple transfer rule (along the lines of brother → frère).

These are problems for general vocabulary. One should note, however, that these problems do not occur for all kinds of vocabulary. In particular, in domains where there is a codified system of terminology, the conceptual organization is generally relatively clear. In such cases, the set of concepts, and thus at least some of the vocabulary of the interlingua, is already settled. Interlinguas are rather metaphysical things. Implicitly or explicitly, they say what the universe is made of (events, processes, individuals, relations, etc.) and how it is put together. It is not at all surprising that many aspects of interlinguas are in dispute and are likely to remain so for some time to come. Given these difficulties, interlinguas in the sense described here are more popular as a basis for theoretical research in MT rather than for full-scale commercial development. For the next few years, most general purpose LK MT systems on the market are unlikely to analyse any deeper than to the level of semantic relations — and even that will be considered impractically deep by many developers and vendors. Nonetheless, we can certainly expect a tendency towards increasingly deep analysis over the next decade or so.

4.3.3   LK Engines Summarised

Having looked at some of the components of an LK engine and having seen something of how they might work, we can conclude this discussion of MT architectures by setting out what the performance characteristics of an LK engine might be.

- Because the system has a (partial) grammar of the target language, output will tend to be grammatical. At any rate, it will be far less strange and far less source-language grammar- dependent than output from transformer engines.

- Because the comparative grammar *completely* specifies a relationship between representations of two languages, translational quality will tend to be more reliable than for transformer engines.

- Because the system tends to separate language into separate modules (one grammar for each language and one comparative grammar for each pair of languages), it is relatively easy in principle to add new languages to the system. For example, adding Dutch to a German-English system would require only the addition of a Dutch grammar module and Dutch-English and German-English comparative grammar modules. Individual language modules can be designed and constructed without specifying which other language modules they will have to work with in the final system. Of course, this matters more to the developer than the user since it is the former that writes and supplies basic language modules.

- The system will be upset by unusual, marginally acceptable or frankly unacceptable input sentences because it has a grammar for the source language and hence a strong notion of grammaticality.

- Because the grammars that computational linguists are able to write are invariably less complete than the 'real' complete grammar of any language, there will be some complicated grammatical input sentences that the system fails to recognise.

From the engine manufacturer's point of view, the transformer architecture has the advantage that it accepts anything that is given to it (though the translations it produces are another matter). The LK architecture is at a disadvantage here: because it thinks it knows something about the languages involved, it tends to think that anything it doesn't know isn't language and hence unacceptable. As a consequence, a pure LK engine during its development phase tends to grind to a halt on anything unusual, or even on something quite common which the developer has forgotten to include.

For commercial purposes, this means that pure LK engines must be supplemented with various coping strategies. For example, if they cannot parse a particular sentence completely, then they at least ought to be able to use some of the information on those parts of the sentence for which they did find a parse — and perhaps they can guess how those well-parsed bits might be fitted together.

LK systems are clearly superior *in principle* to transformers. However, MT systems require a considerable development effort and some commercial transformer systems which have undergone extensive revision, refinement and updating over the years can achieve a good overall performance. Furthermore, some MT systems have sufficient flexibility in the design of the engine to allow developers to increase the depth and sophistication of their linguistic knowledge and even the overall arrangement of grammars. We can therefore expect highly developed transformer MT systems to survive in some sectors of the marketplace for some years to come.

4.4 Summary

In this chapter we have looked inside two different kinds of MT system, transformer systems, and linguistic knowledge systems, discussing, under the latter heading the distinction between transfer and interlingual systems. The following chapters will amplify this picture in various ways, by looking in more detail at the sorts of knowledge that are involved, for example, in dictionaries, and the representation of 'meaning', and looking at some particular translation problems. In Chapter 10 we will give some more discussion of the limitations of LK approaches, and describe a recently developed alternative.

4.5 Further Reading

Probably the most famous example of a system with what we have called a transformer architecture is SYSTRAN. This is described in [Hutchins and Somers, 1992]. A recent discussion can be found in [Wilks, 1992].

A more detailed overview of transfer systems can be found in [Arnold, 1993].

Examples of transfer systems include the following, ARIANE [Vauquois and Boitet, 1985], SUSY [Maas, 1987], MU (the Japanese National Project) [Nagao *et al.*,

July 1986], METAL [Slocum *et al.*, 1987], [Bennett and Slocum, 1988], TAUM-AVIATION [Isabelle, 1987], ETAP-2 [Apresian *et al.*, 1992], LMT [McCord, 1989], EUROTRA [Arnold, 1986; Arnold and des Tombe, 1987; Copeland *et al.*, 1991a; Copeland *et al.*, 1991b], , CAT-2 [Sharp, 1988], MIMO [Arnold and Sadler, 1990], MIMO-2 [van Noord *et al.*, 1990], ELU [Estival *et al.*, 1990]. Several of these systems are discussed in detail in [Hutchins and Somers, 1992].

Among interlingual systems, the following are noteworthy: Rosetta [Landsbergen, 1987b; Landsbergen, 1987a], KBMT [Goodman, 1989], [Goodman and Nirenburg, 1991]. A recent overview is given in [Nirenburg, 1993]. [Hutchins and Somers, 1992, Chapter 6] is also recommended. One interlingual approach that we have not mentioned here is that which uses a human language as the interlingual. The best known example of this is DLT, which uses Esperanto, see [Schubert, 1992] and [Hutchins and Somers, 1992, Chapter 17].

Chapter 5

Dictionaries

5.1 Introduction

This Chapter is about the role played by dictionaries in MT. Our decision to devote a whole chapter to this discussion reflects the importance of dictionaries in MT:

- Dictionaries are the largest components of an MT system in terms of the amount of information they hold. If they are more then simple word lists (and they should be, if a system is to perform well), then they may well be the most expensive components to construct.

- More than any other component, the size and quality of the dictionary limits the scope and coverage of a system, and the quality of translation that can be expected.

- The dictionaries are where the end user can expect to be able to contribute most to a system — in fact, an end user can expect to have to make some additions to system dictionaries to make a system really useful. While MT suppliers rarely make it possible for users to modify other components, they normally expect them to make additions to the dictionary. Thus, from the point of view of a user, a basic understanding of dictionary construction and sensitivity to the issues involved in 'describing words' is an important asset.

- In discussing dictionaries here, we include also some discussion of terminology — it is with respect to the treatment of terminology that MT provides some of its most useful benefits.

We shall approach the question of dictionaries in MT obliquely, by considering in some detail the information contained in, and issues raised by, the paper dictionaries with which we are all familiar. There are a number of reasons for this, but the most important is that the dictionaries in existing MT systems are diverse in terms of formats, coverage, level of detail and precise formalism for lexical description. This diversity should not be a surprise. Different theories of linguistic representation can give rise to different views of the dictionary, and different implementation strategies can make even fundamentally similar views of the dictionary look very different in detail. Moreover, the different kinds of MT engine obviously put quite different requirements on the contents of the dictionary. For example, dictionaries in an interlingual system need not contain any translation information *per se*, all that is necessary is to associate words with the appropriate (collections of) interlingual concepts. By contrast, transformer systems will typically give information about source language items, and their translations, including perhaps information that is really about the target language, and which is necessary to trigger certain transformations (e.g. to do with the placement of particles like *up* in *look it up*, and *look up the answer*). Since transfer systems typically use more abstract levels of representation, the associated dictionaries have to contain information about these levels. Moreover, in a transfer system, especially one which is intended to deal with several languages, it is common to separate monolingual dictionaries for source and target languages (which give information about the various levels of representation involved in analysis and synthesis), from bilingual dictionaries which are involved in transfer (which normally relate source and target lexical items, and which normally contain information only about the levels of representation that are involved in transfer).

We would like to abstract away from these divergences and points of detail in order to focus on the main issues. Accordingly, we will begin with a brief discussion of typical entries that one might find in a good monolingual 'paper' dictionary, and a good bilingual 'paper' dictionary.[1] We will then briefly discuss the sort of information about words that one typically finds in MT dictionaries, outlining some of the different ways such information can be represented. As we have said, a simple view is that a dictionary is a list of words. However, it is impractical, and perhaps impossible to provide an exhaustive list of words for most languages. This is because of the possibility of forming new words out of existing ones, by various morphological processes. In Section 5.4 we will look briefly at these, and provide some discussion of how they can be dealt with, and the problems they raise in an MT context. In Section 5.5 we will briefly describe the difference between terminology and general vocabulary.

5.2 Paper Dictionaries

The best place to start our discussion is by looking at typical entries that one might find in a monolingual English dictionary (cf. page 89), and a bilingual dictionary

---

[1]'Paper' here is intended to convey 'intended for human readers', as opposed to 'electronic' meaning 'intended for use by computers'. Of course, it is possible for a paper dictionary to be stored on a computer like any other document, and our use of 'paper' here is not supposed to exclude this. If one were being precise, one should distinguish 'paper' dictionaries, 'machine readable' dictionaries (conventional dictionaries which are stored on, and can therefore be accessed automatically by computer), and 'machine *usable* dictionaries'.

(cf. page 90). [2]

A Monolingual Dictionary Entry

but.ton /'bʌtn/ *n* **1** knob or disc made of wood, metal, etc sewn onto a garment as a fastener or as an ornament: *a coat, jacket, shirt, trouser button* ∘ *lose a button* ∘ *sew on a new button* ∘ *do one's buttons up* ⇒ illus at JACKET. **2** small knob that is pressed to operate a doorbell, a switch on a machine, etc: *Which button do I press to turn the radio on?* **3**(idm) **bright as a button** ⇒ BRIGHT. **on the 'button** (*US infml*) precisely: *You've got it on the button!*

▷ **but.ton** *v* **1**(a)[Tn,Tn.p] ~**sth(up)** fasten sth with buttons: *button (up) one's coat, jacket, shirt, etc.* (b)[I,Ip] ~**(up)** be fastened with buttons: *This dress buttons at the back.* **2**(idm) **button (up) one's lip** (*US sl*) be silent. **3**(phr v) **button sth up** (*infml*) complete sth successfully: *The deal should be buttoned up by tomorrow.*

□ **,buttoned 'up** silent and reserved; shy: *I've never met anyone so buttoned up.*

,button-down 'collar collar with ends that are fastened to the shirt with buttons.

'buttonhole *n* **1** slit through which a button is passed to fasten clothing. ⇒ illus at JACKET. **2** flower worn in the buttonhole of the lapel of a coat or jacket. - *v*[Tn] make (sb) stop and listen, often reluctantly, to what one wants to say.

'buttonhook *n* hook for pulling a button into place through a buttonhole.

,button 'mushroom small unopened mushroom.

We will start by looking at the layout of the first half of the monolingual entry. The entry for *button* starts off with the word itself in bold print. This is called the *head word*. The dot in the word indicates where the word may be broken off (e.g. for hyphenation). After that there is a phonetic transcription of the word's pronunciation. Then the entry falls into two main parts, describing first the noun and then the verb *button*. Definitions identify two different meanings, or *readings* of the noun *button*, with examples of usage given in italics. The ⇒ refers the reader to a related entry. Idiomatic expressions are given under **3**. As for the verb, the code [Tn,Tn.p] indicates that the verb is transitive, i.e. appears in a sentence with a subject and an object (Tn), or is transitive with an adverbial particle (Tn.p).

---

[2]The form of the monolingual entry is based on that used in the *Oxford Advanced Learner's Dictionary* (OALD); the bilingual entry is similar to what one finds in *Collins-Robert English-French dictionary*.

In this case the adverbial particle is the preposition *up*. Under **b** another usage is described where *button* is an intransitive verb and thus takes only a subject (I), or a subject plus the preposition *up* (Ip). Idioms appear under **2**. The box halfway through the entry signals the start of a list of complex forms, a phrasal verb (*button up*), and several compounds, which we will discuss later in this chapter. The verb, and noun, phrasal verbs and compounds are given in a standard form (the *citation* form), with information about stress (given by raised or lowered apostrophes). By convention, this is normally the singular form of nouns, and the infinitive form of verbs (i.e. the form that one finds after *to*, as in *to button*, *to be*, etc.)

Two Bilingual Dictionary Entries

button ['bʌtn] **1** *n* **(a)** (*garment, door, bell, lamp, fencing foil*) bouton *m*. **chocolate** ~s pastilles *fpl* de chocolate. **2** *vt* (*also* ~ **up**) *garment* boutonner. **3** *vi* (*garment*) se boutonner. **4** *cpd* **buttonhook** tirebouton *m*; **button mushroom** (petit) champignon *m* de couche *or* de Paris.

printer ['prɪntə] *n* **(a)** imprimeur *m*; (*typographer*) typographe *mf*, imprimeur. **the text has gone to the** ~ le texte est chez l'imprimeur; ~'s **devil** apprenti imprimeur; ~'s **error** faute *f* d'impression, coquille *f*; ~'s **ink** encre *f* d'imprimerie; ~'s **reader** correcteur *m*, -trice *f* (d'épreuves). **(b)** (*Comput*) imprimante *f*. **(c)** (*Phot*) tifeuse *f*.

The bilingual entry for the noun *printer* begins with the head word, its pronunciation and word class, in this case noun. Logically, the entry then divides into three component parts **(a)**, **(b)**, and **(c)**, essentially distinguishing three different uses or meaning of the noun in English which have distinct translations into French. Where a particular meaning can be identified by reference to a subject field, this information is given (bracketed, in italics) — here computation and photography are identified as subject fields. If the context of use is other than these two fields, then the translation given under **(a)** is assumed to be appropriate. For each reading, the gender of the translation is given: *m* or *f* (for *masculine* or *feminine*, *mf* indicates either is possible; where the masculine and feminine forms differ, both are indicated — *printer's reader* is thus either *correcteur* or *correctrice*). If two different translations are possible they are both given, separated by a comma (thus, either *typographe*, or *imprimeur* are possible 'general' translations). The entry also contains some examples of idioms, or other usages, again with the appropriate translations.

Normal, 'paper' dictionaries, are collections of entries such as these. That is, they are basically lists of words, with information about the various properties. While grammar rules define all the possible linguistic structures in a language, the descriptions of individual words that are found in the dictionary or dictionaries state which words can appear in which of the different structures. A common (though not completely correct) view is that dictionaries contain all the 'idiosyncratic', 'irregular', or unpredictable information about words, while grammars provide general rules about classes of word, and phrases (this is only true if one excludes morphological rules and idioms from the dictionary — the former can be viewed as dealing with classes of word, and the latter are phrases).

One can get an idea of the sheer volume of information of this kind that may be needed by considering that for commercial purposes a lexicon with 20 000 entries is often considered as the minimum. This however is still only a modest percentage of existing words — the *Oxford English Dictionary* contains about 250 000 entries without being exhaustive even of general usage.[3] In fact, no dictionary can ever be really complete. Not only do dictionaries generally restrict themselves to either general, or specialist technical vocabulary (but not both), in addition, new words are constantly being coined, borrowed, used in new senses, and formed by normal morphological processes.[4]

5.3 Types of Word Information

We have already observed that dictionaries are a, perhaps *the*, central component of MT systems. In earlier Chapters, we have presented a highly simplified view of dictionaries — for example, in Chapter 3 the dictionary was sometimes little more than a list of rules such as v → walk, which only allows information about part of speech to be represented, and in Chapter 4 we gave translation rules which simply paired up the citation forms of source and target words (e.g. temperature ↔ temperatur). However, though some of the information that is found in a typical paper dictionary is of limited value in MT (e.g. information about pronunciation is only useful in speech to speech systems), in general the quality and detail of the information one needs for MT is at least equal to that which one finds in paper dictionaries. In this section we discuss the various pieces of information about words that a good MT system must contain, basing ourselves on the dictionary entries above. An issue we will not address in this Chapter is the treatment of idioms, which one typically finds in paper dictionary entries. We discuss the treatment of idioms in Chapter 6.

It is useful to make a distinction between the characteristics of a word itself (its

---

[3] One can also get some idea of the *cost* of dictionary construction from this. Even if one were able to write four entries an hour, and keep this up for 8 hours a day every working day, it would still take over three years to construct even a small size dictionary. Of course, the time it takes to write a dictionary entry is very variable, depending on how much of the work has already been done by other lexicographers.

[4] In fact, it is arguable that the vocabulary of a language like English, with relatively productive morphological processes, is infinite, in the sense that there is no longest word of the language. Even the supposedly longest word *antidisestablishmentarianism* can be made longer by adding a prefix such as *crypto-*, or a suffix such as *-ist*. The result may not be pretty, but it is arguably a possible word of English. The point is even clearer when one considers compound words (see Section 5.4.3.

inherent properties) and the restrictions it places on other words in its grammatical environment. Although this distinction is not explicitly drawn in paper dictionaries, information of both types is available in them. Information about grammatical properties includes the indication of gender in the French part of the bilingual dictionary entry, and the indication of number on nouns (typically, the citation form of nouns is the singular form, and information about number is only explicitly given for nouns which have only plural forms, such as *scissors*, and *trousers*).

Information about the grammatical environment a word can appear in is normally thought of as dividing into two kinds: **subcategorization** information, which indicates the syntactic environments that a word can occur in, and **selectional restrictions** which describe semantic properties of the environment. Typical information about subcategorization is the information that *button* is a transitive verb. This is expressed in the verb code [Tn] in the dictionary entry on page 89. More precisely, this indicates that it is a verb that appears as the HEAD of sentences with a (noun phrase) SUBJECT and a (noun phrase) OBJECT. The following gives some examples, together with the appropriate verb codes from OALD:

(1) a. The president died. [I]

  b. The Romans destroyed the city. [Tn]

  c. Sam gave roses to Kim. [Dn.pr]

  d. Sam gave Kim roses. [Dn.n]

  e. Sam persuaded Kim to stay at home. [Cn.t]

  f. Kim believed that the library was closed. [Tf]

  g. The quality is low. [La]

  h. Sam appeared the best man for the job. [Ln]

Note that [I] refers to intransitive verbs that only need a subject to form a grammatical sentence, [Tn] to transitive verbs (like *button*) that need a subject and an object, [Dn.pr] to ditransitive verbs which take a subject and two objects, where the second one is introduced by the preposition *to*, [Dn.n] to ditransitive verbs that take a subject plus two object nouns, [Cn.t] to complex transitive verbs which require a subject, object and an infinitival (non-tensed) clause introduced by *to*, [Tf] to transitive verbs taking a subject, object and a finite (tensed) sentence introduced by *that*, [La] to linking verbs which link an adjectival phrase (which describes in some way the subject), to the subject, and [Ln] refers to linking verbs which link a noun phrase to the subject.

Verbs are not the only word categories that subcategorize for certain elements in their environment. Nouns exhibit the same phenomenon, like those nouns that have been derived from verbs (deverbal nouns).

(2) a. *The death of the president* shocked everybody.

b. *The destruction of the city by the Romans* was thorough.

Similarly, there are some adjectives that subcategorize for certain complements. Note that in the examples below we find three different types of complements, and that 3b and 3c differ from each other because in 3b the subject of the main clause is also the understood subject of the subclause, whereas in 3c the subject of the main clause is the understood object of the subclause.

(3) a. Mary was *proud of her performance.*

b. He was *eager to unwrap his present.*

c. That matter is *easy to deal with.*

An adequate dictionary of English would probably have to recognize at least twenty different subcategorization classes of verb, and a similar number for adjectives and nouns.

The reason one cannot be precise about the number of different subcategorization classes is that it depends (a) on how fine the distinctions are that one wants to draw, and (b) on how far one relies on rules or general principles to capture regularities. For example, probably all verbs allow coordinated subjects such as *Sam and Leslie,* but there are some, like *meet*, where this is equivalent to an ordinary transitive SUBJECT-VERB-OBJECT construction (cf. (4a), and (4b) mean the same, but (4c) and (4d) do not). One could decide to recognise this distinction by creating a separate subcategorization class, thus extending the number of classes. But one could also argue that this fact about *meet* and similar verbs is probably related to their semantics (they describe symmetric relations, in the sense that if A meets B, then B meets A), and is thus regular and predictable. The appropriate approach could then be to treat it by means of a general linguistic rule (perhaps one that transforms structures like (4a) into ones of the form (4b)) Of course, unless one can rely on semantic information to pick out verbs like *meet*, one will have to introduce some mark on such verbs to ensure that they, and only they, undergo this rule. However, this is not necessarily the same as introducing a subcategorization class.

(4) a. Sam met Mary

b. Sam and Mary met

c. Sam saw Mary

d. *Sam and Mary saw

Subcategorization information indicates that, for example, the verb *button* occurs with a noun phrase OBJECT. In fact, we know much more about the verb than this — the OBJECT, or in terms of semantic roles, the PATIENT, of the verb has to be a 'buttonable' thing, such as a piece of clothing, and that the SUBJECT (more precisely AGENT) of the verb is normally animate.[5] Such information is commonly referred to as the **selectional restrictions** that words place on items that appear in constructions where they are the HEAD. This information is implicit in the paper dictionary entry above — the information that the object of *button* is inanimate, and normally an item of clothing has to be worked out from the use of *sth* (= 'some*thing*') in the definition, and the example, which gives *coat, jacket, shirt* as possibilities. The entry nowhere says the SUBJECT of the verb has to be an animate entity (probably human), since no other entity can perform the action of 'buttoning'. It is assumed (rightly) that the human reader can work this sort of thing out for herself. This information has to be made explicit if it is to be used in analysis, transfer or synthesis, of course.

Basic inherent information and information about subcategorization and selectional restrictions can be represented straightforwardly for MT purposes. Essentially, entries in an MT dictionary will be equivalent to collections of attributes and values (i.e. features). For example, one might have something like the following for the noun *button*, indicating that its base, or citation form is button, that it is a common noun, which is concrete (rather than abstract, like *happiness*, or *sincerity*)

```
lex = button
cat = n
ntype = common
number =
human = no
concrete = yes
```

An obvious way to implement such things is as records in a database, with attributes naming fields (e.g. cat), and values as the contents of the fields (e.g. n). But it is not always necessary to name the field — one could, for example, adopt a convention that the first field in a record always contains the citation form (in this case the value of the feature lex), that the second field indicates the category, and that the third field some sort of subdivision of the category.

Looking at the dictionary entry for the noun *button* it becomes clear that different parts of speech will have a different collection of attributes. For example, verbs will have a vtype, rather than an ntype feature, and while verbs might have fields for indications of number, person and tense, one would not expect to find such fields for prepositions. In the entry we have given we also find one attribute — number — without a value. The idea here is to indicate that a value for this attribute is possible, but is not inherent to the word *button*, which may have different number

---

[5]The restriction applying on the OBJECT of the verb actually concerns the thing which is *buttoned* whether that appears as the OBJECT of a active sentence or the SUBJECT of a passive sentence.

values on different occasions (unlike e.g. *trousers*, which is always plural). Of course, this sort of blank field is essential if fields are indicated by position, rather than name. In systems which name attribute fields it might simply be equivalent to omitting the attribute, but maintaining the field is still useful because it helps someone who has to modify the dictionary to understand the information in the dictionary. An alternative to giving a blank value, is to follow the practice of some paper dictionaries and fill in the default, or (in some sense) normal value. For an attribute like number, this would presumably be singular. This alternative, however, is unfashionable these days, since it goes against the generally accepted idea that in the best case linguistic processing only *adds*, and never changes information. The attraction of such an approach is that it makes the order in which things are done less critical (cf. our remarks about the desirability of separating declarative and procedural information in Chapter 4).

In order to include information about subcategorization and selectional restrictions, one has two options. The first is to encode it via sets of attributes with atomic values such as those above. In practice, this would mean that one might have features such as subcat=subj_obj, and sem_patient=clothing. As regards subcategorization information, this is essentially the approach used in the monolingual paper dictionary above. The resulting dictionary entry could then look something like the following:

```
lex = button
cat = v
vtype = main
finite =
person =
number =
subcat = subj_obj
sem_agent = human
sem_patient = clothing
```

In some systems this may be the only option. However, some systems may allow values to be sets, or lists, in which case one has more flexibility. For example, one might represent subcategorization information by means of a list of categories, for example subcat = [np,np,np] might indicate a verb that allows three NPs (such as *give*), and [np,np,pp] might indicate a verb that takes two NPs and a PP (again like *give*).

(5) a. Sam gave roses to Kim. (subcat = [np,np,pp])
     b. Sam gave Kim roses. (subcat = [np,np,np])

A further refinement would be to indicate the actual grammatical relations involved, perhaps as in subcat = [SUBJ:np, OBJ:np, IOBJ:pp]. A notation which allows the lexicographer to indicate other properties of the items would be still more expressive. For example, it would be useful to indicate that with *give*, the preposition in the PP has to be *to*. This would mean that instead of 'pp' and 'np' one would have collections of features, and perhaps even pieces of syntactic structure. (A current trend in computational linguistics involves the development of formalisms that allow such very detailed lexical entries, and we will say a little more about them in Chapter 10).

Turning now to the treatment of translation information in MT dictionaries, one possibility is to attempt to represent all the relevant information by means of attributes and values. Thus, as an addition to the dictionary entry for *button* given above, a transformer system could specify a 'translation' feature which has as its value the appropriate target language word; e.g. `trans = bouton` for translation into French. One might also include features which trigger certain transformations (for example for changing word order for certain words). However, this is not a particularly attractive view. For one thing, it is clearly oriented in one direction, and it will be difficult to produce entries relating to the other direction of translation from such entries. More generally, one wants a bilingual dictionary to allow the replacement of certain source language oriented information with corresponding target language information — i.e. replace the information one derives from the source dictionary by information derived from the target dictionary. This suggests the usage of translation rules which relate head words to head words. That is, rules of the type we introduced in Chapter 4, like `temperature ↔ temperatur`.

As we noted before, not all translation rules can be a simple mapping of source language words onto their target language equivalents. One will have to put conditions on the rules. For example, one might like to be able to describe in the bilingual entry that deals with *like* and *plaire*, the change in grammatical relations that occurs if one is working with relatively shallow levels of representation,. In effect, the transfer rule that we gave for this example in Chapter 4 might be seen as a bilingual lexical entry. Other translation rules that may require more than just a simple pairing of source and target words are those that treat phenomena like idioms and compounds, and some cases of lexical holes (cf. Chapter 6). To deal with such phenomena bilingual dictionary entries may have a single lexical item on the side of one language, whereas the other side describes a (possibly quite complex) linguistic structure.

The entry for *button* taken from a paper dictionary at the beginning of this Chapter illustrates an issue of major importance to the automatic processing of some languages, including English. This is the very widespread occurrence of **homography** in the language. Loosely speaking, homographs are words that are written in the same way. However, it is important to distinguish several different cases (sometimes the term homography is restricted to only one of them).

1 The case where what is intuitively a single noun (for example) has several different readings. This can be seen with the entry for *button* on page 89,

where a reading relating to clothing is distinguished from a 'knob' reading.

2 The case where one has related items of different categories which are written alike. For example, *button* can be either a noun or a verb.

3 The case where one has what appears to be unrelated items which happen to be written alike. The classic example of this is the noun *bank*, which can designate either the side of a river, or a financial institution.

These distinctions have practical significance when one is writing (creating, extending, or modifying) a dictionary, since they relate to the question of when one should create a new entry (by defining a new headword). The issues involved are rather different when one is creating a 'paper' dictionary (where issues of readability are paramount) or a dictionary for MT, but it is in any case very much a pragmatic decision. One good guiding principle one might adopt is to group entries hierarchically in terms of amounts of shared information. For example, there is relatively little that the two senses of *bank* share apart from their citation form and the fact that they are both common nouns, so one may as well associate them with different entries. In a computational setting where one has to give unique names to different entries, this will involve creating headwords such as bank_1 and bank_2, or (bank_finance, and bank_river). As regards the noun and verb *button*, though one might want to have some way of indicating that they are related, they do not share much information, and can therefore be treated as separate entries. For multiple readings of a word, for example, the two readings of the noun *button*, on the other hand, most information is shared — they differ mainly in their semantics. In this case, it might be useful to impose an organization in the lexicon in which information can be inherited from an entry into sub-entries (or more generally, from one entry to another), or to see them as subentries of an abstract 'protoentry' of some sort. This will certainly save time and effort in dictionary construction — though the savings one makes may look small in one case, it becomes significant when multiplied by the number items that have different readings (this is certainly in the thousands, perhaps the hundreds of thousands, since most words listed in normal dictionaries have at least two readings). The issues this raises are complex and we cannot do them justice here, however, the following will give a flavour of what is involved.

More generally, what one is talking about here is **inheritance** of properties between entries (or from entries into subentries). This is illustrated in Figure 5.1. One could imagine extending this, introducing abstract entries expressing information true of *classes* of (real) entry. For example, one might want to specify certain facts about all nouns (all noun readings) just once, rather than stating them separately in each entry. The entry for a typical noun might then be very simple, saying no more than 'this is a typical noun', and giving the citation form (and semantics, and translation, if appropriate). One allows for subregularities (that is lexical elements which are regular in some but not all properties), by allowing elements to inherit some information while expressing the special or irregular information directly in the entry itself. In many cases, the optimal organization can turn out to be quite complicated, with entries inheriting from a number of different sources. Such an approach becomes even more attractive if default inheritance is possible. That is, that information is inherited, unless it is explicitly contradicted in an entry/reading — it would then be possible to say, for example, 'this is a typical noun, except for the way it forms its plural'.

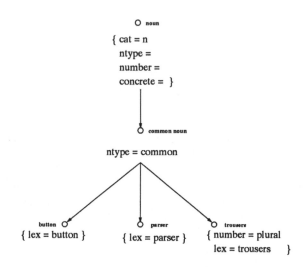

Figure 5.1 Inheritance

One final and important component of an MT dictionary, which is entirely lacking in paper dictionaries (at least in their printed, public form) is *documentation*. Apart from general documentation describing design decisions, and terminology, and providing lists and definitions (including operational tests) for the attributes and values that are used in the dictionary (it is, obviously, essential that such terms are used consistently — and consistency is a problem since creating and maintaining a dictionary is not a task that can be performed by a single individual), it is important that each entry include some lexicographers' comments — information about who created the entry, when it was last revised, the kinds of example it is based on, what problems there are with it, and the sorts of improvement that are required. Such information is vital if a dictionary is to be maintained and extended. In general, though the quality and quantity of such documentation has no effect on the actual performance of the dictionary, it is critical if a dictionary is to be modified or extended.

5.4   Dictionaries and Morphology

Morphology is concerned with the internal structure of words, and how words can be formed. It is usual to recognize three different word formation processes.

1 **Inflectional** processes, by means of which a word is derived from another word form, acquiring certain grammatical features but maintaining the same part of speech or category (e.g. *walk, walks*);

2 **Derivational** processes in which a word of a different category is derived from another word or word stem by the application of some process (e.g. *grammar* ↦ *grammatical, grammatical* ↦ *grammaticality*);

3 **Compounding**, in which independent words come together in some way to form a new unit (*buttonhole*).

In English, inflectional and derivational processes involve **prefixes** (as in *undo*) and **suffixes** (as in *stupidity*), and what is called **conversion**, or **zero-affixation** where there is a change of category, but no change of form (and example would be the process that relates the noun *button* to the verb). In other languages, a range of devices such as changes in the vowel patterns of words, doubling or reduplication of syllables, etc., are also found. Clearly, these prefixes and suffixes (collectively known as **affixes**) cannot 'stand alone' as words. Compounding is quite different in that the parts can each occur as individual words. Compounding is a very productive phenomenon in the Germanic languages, and poses some particular problems in MT, which we will discuss later.

5.4.1 Inflection

As a rule, paper dictionaries abstract away from inflection. Head words are generally uninflected, that is, nouns appear in singular form and verbs have the base (or infinitival) form. There are a number of reasons for this. The first is that inflection is a relatively regular process, and once the exceptional cases have been separated out, inflectional processes apply to all members of a given category. For example, to form the third person singular of the present tense of verbs one simply suffixes *s* (or its variant *es*) to the citation form of the verb. There are very few exceptions to this rule. Since it is a regular process, the dictionary user can be relied upon to form regularly inflected words from the citation forms given in the dictionary at will. Of course, irregularities, such as irregular plurals (*sheep, oxen, phenomena*, etc.) and plural only nouns (*trousers*) must be stated explicitly. A second important reason is eminently practical — it saves space, time and effort in constructing entries. Since English inflectional morphology is rather impoverished, these savings are not enormous. But Spanish, for example, has six different verb forms for the present tense, and if we add those for the past tense (either imperfecto or pretérito in Spanish) it amounts to 16 different verb forms. Other languages make even more use of inflections, like, for example, Finnish where there are said to be in the region of 2000 forms for most nouns, and 12 000 forms for each verb. It will be obvious that the need to describe inflectional variation by means of rules is pressing in such cases.

Within the context of MT, it is clearly desirable to have a similar approach, where monolingual and transfer dictionaries only contain the head words and no inflected words. In order to achieve this a system must be capable of capturing the regular patterns of inflection. This can be done by adding a morphological component to the system, which describes all the regular inflections in general rules, with additional explicit rules for irregular inflection, thus allowing dictionary writers to abstract away from inflected forms as much as possible. The morphological component will be able to map inflected words onto the appropriate head words and will retain the information provided by the inflectional affix by adding the relevant features.

Let us consider again the verb *affects* in the simple sentence *Temperature affects density*. First, we want our morphological component to recognize *affects* as an inflected form of *affect*. Secondly, we want to retain the information carried by the affix so we can use it later when generating the output sentence. In the case of *affects* this means we want to state that the verb is finite, or tensed (in fact, present tense). This is important since it allows the verb to occur as the only verb of a main clause. The tense also prevents the verb from occurring behind auxiliary verbs like *will.* Other information that we gather from the inflection is the fact that the verb is third person (as opposed to first person, occurring with *I* or *we*, and as opposed with second person, occurring with *you*), and that it is singular (rather than third person plural, which occurs with *they*, or with a plural noun).

There are various ways of describing this, but perhaps the simplest is to use rules of the following form:[6]

(lex=V,cat=v,+finite,person=3rd,number=sing,tense=pres) ↔ V+ s

Here we have introduced a rule which says that finite verbs which are third person singular and have present tense (cat=v, +finite, person=3rd, number=sing, tense=pres) can be formed by adding s to the base form (the base form is represented as the value of the attribute lex). The rule can also be read in the opposite direction: if a word can be divided into a string of characters and *s*, then it may be a finite verb with third person singular in present tense. Other rules would have to be given to indicate that the +s ending can be added to all verbs, except for those that end in +s, themselves,[7] in which case es is added (cf. *kiss, kisses*).

Whether something is indeed the base form of the verb can be verified in the monolingual dictionary. So, if the morphological analyser encounters a word like *affects*, it will check whether the monolingual dictionary contains an entry with the features cat = v, lex = affect. Since it does, *affects* can be represented by means of the

---

[6]In this rule we write +finite for finite=+. We also ignore some issues about datatypes, in particular, the fact that on the right-hand-side V stands for a string of characters, while on the lefthand (lexical) side it stands for the value of an attribute, which is probably an atom, rather than a string.

[7]More precisely, the rule is that the third person singular form is the base form plus *s*, except (i) when the base form ends in *s, ch, sh, o, x, z,* in which case +es is added (for example, *poach-poaches, push-pushes*), and (ii) when the base form ends in *y,* when *ies* is added to the base minus *y.*

lexical entry, with some of the information supplied by the rule.The result of morphological analysis then is a representation which consists of both the information provided by the dictionary and the information contributed by the affix.

```
lex = affect
cat = v
vtype = main
subcat = subj_obj
sem_agent = ?
sem_patient = ?
vform = finite
person = 3rdsing
tense = pres
```

In order to recognize irregular forms the morphological component has to contain explicit rules. One approach here is to try to normalise the spelling, so that the ordinary morphological rules can deal with the result. For example, one might have rules like the following to deal with the irregular third person singular forms of *be* and *have*.

be+s → is

have+s → has

Under this approach, morphological analysis for *is* and *has* is a two stage process.

The alternative is to state the relationship between the forms *is* and *has* directly, via rules like the following:

(lex=be,cat=v,+finite,person=3rd,number=sing,tense=pres) ↔ is

(lex=have,cat=v,+finite,person=3rd,number=sing,tense=pres) ↔ has

A graphic interpretation of the two alternative approaches is given in Figure 5.2.

Notice that we must ensure that these rules apply in the right cases. For example, *dies* should not be analysed as *di+es*. This is not problematic, providing we ensure that the analyses we produce contain actual lexical items.[8]

In synthesis, there is a related problem of making sure that the regular rules do not produce *bes, and *haves. One approach to this is to try to divide rules into

---

[8] Notice, however, that we still cannot expect morphological analysis and lexical lookup to come up with a single right answer straight away. Apart from anything else, a form like *affects* could be a noun rather than a verb. For another thing, just looking at the word form in isolation will not tell us which of several readings of a word is involved.

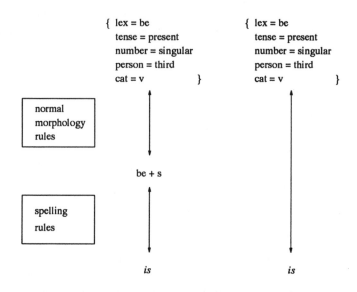

Figure 5.2 Treatment of Irregular Verbs

exceptional and default groups, and to make sure that no default rule applies if a an exceptional rule can apply. Thus, for example, the fact that there is a special rule for the third person singular form of *is* would prevent the application of the normal or default rule that simply adds *s* to the base form of the verb.

Alternatively, one could add features to control which rules apply to lexical entries, and have the morphological rules check for the presence of the particular feature. This approach is particularly attractive in cases where a language has a number of conjugation or declension classes — lexical items can contain features indicating their conjugation/declension class, which the morphological rules can check.

So far, we have talked about morphological rules as things that actually apply as a sentence is being analysed. Another way in which one could use them is to compile out a full form dictionary from a dictionary of uninflected words, essentially by running the morphological rules over the dictionary of uninflected forms. Note, however, that this strategy would build a monolingual dictionary of an enormous size for languages like Spanish, or Finnish.

5.4.2   Derivation

Derivation processes form new words (generally of a different category) from existing words, in English this is mainly done by adding affixes. For example, *industrialization*, and *destruction* can be thought of as being derived in the way illustrated below. As one can see from *destruction*, it is not necessarily the citation form of a word that appears in derivations, for this reason it is common to talk of derivational processes involving stems and affixes (rather than words and affixes).

(6) a. $[_N [_V [_{ADJ} [_N$ industry $]+$ial $]+$ize $]+$ation $]$
    b. $[_N [_V$ destroy $]+$ion $]$

In a paper dictionary, some derived words are listed, under the relevant head word. This is partly because affixes differ in their productivity and in the regularity of the effect they have on the words or stems that they combine with. For example, there seems to be no real basis on which to predict which of the noun-forming affixes produce nouns from particular verbs. This is illustrated below by the verbs *arrive*, *destroy*, and *deport*:

(7)

Verb	+al	+uction	+ation
arrive	arrival	*arruction	*arrivation
destroy	*destroyal	destruction	*destroyation
deport	*deportal	*depuction	deportation

However, some derivational processes are quite regular and can be described by means of a bf word grammar. This involves: (i) entering the affix in the dictionary; (ii) allowing it to subcategorize for what it combines with (e.g. *-able* combines with transitive verbs: witness *read-readable*) — this is just like normal syntactic subcategorization; (iii) making sure that the rules to combine words and affixes give the derived word the correct features for the result, and take care of any spelling changes in word or affix; (iv) finding some way of specifying the meaning in terms of the meanings of the word and affix.

As with inflection, the rules must be set up so as to produce only genuine lexical items. For example, we can ensure that the rules that analyse *cordiality* as *cordial+-ity* do not produce *qual+-ity* from *quality*, because there is no lexical item **qual*.

One approach to handling derivational morphology in MT is to simply list all derived words, and for some derived words (e.g. *landing*, in the sense of area at the top of stairs), this is clearly the right approach, because their meaning is unpredictable. But not all derivational morphology is unpredictable. Some affixes almost always have just one sense, like the prefix *un* which (when combined with an adjective) normally means 'not X' (*unhappy* means *not happy*)[9], and for others there are certain tendencies or regularities: with the examples in (8) the addition of the suffix *-ing* to the verb stem seems to have the same, regular consequence for the meaning of the word, so the derived word denotes the action or process associated with the verb (the act of Xing). Speakers exploit this fact by creating new words which they expect hearers to understand.

---

[9]Note that the category of the stem word is important, since there is another prefix *un* which combines with verbs to give verbs which mean 'perform the reverse action to X' — to *unbutton* is to reverse the effect of buttoning.

(8)   a.   The killing of elephants is forbidden.

    b.   Driving off went without any problems.

    c.   The painting of still lives never appealed to me.

In contrast with the examples in (8), one should consider the nouns in (9), where the meaning, although common, is not predictable from the suffix -*ing*:

(9)   a.   Painting: a picture produced with paint

    b.   Covering: something which covers something

    c.   Cutting: something which has been cut out

    d.   Crossing: a place were e.g. roads cross

We see here that a verb+ing noun can refer to a product (9a), a thing which performs an action (9b), a thing which undergoes an action (9c), or a place (9d). At the same time, however, it is true that in most cases the regular interpretation 'the act of Xing' is *also* available. What this means is that there is almost always a problem of ambiguity with derived words.

Moreover, there are cases where one can translate derived words by translating the stem, and translating the affix. For example, the French translation of English adverbs formed from an adjective plus -*ly* is often made up of the translation of the adjective plus -*ment* (e.g. *quick+ly* → *rapide+ment*, *easy+ly* → *facile+ment*), etc. But this is only possible for some affixes, and only when the interpretation of the derived word is predictable. The difficulties of translating derived words by translating stems and affixes can can be seen from the translation of the previous examples into Dutch.

(10)   a.   killing ⇒ doden

    b.   driving off ⇒ wegrijden

    c.   painting (the act) ⇒ schilderen

    d.   painting (the product) ≠ schilderen, but ⇒ schilderij

    e.   covering ≠ bedekken, but ⇒ bedekking

    f.   cutting ≠ knippen, but ⇒ knipsel

    g.   crossing ≠ kruisen, but ⇒ kruispunt

Thus, though the idea of providing rules for translating derived words may seem attractive, it raises many problems and so it is currently more of a research goal for MT than a practical possibility.

5.4.3 Compounds

A compound is a combination of two or more words which functions as a single word. In English, the most common type of compound is probably a compound made up of two nouns (noun-noun compounds), such as those in the dictionary entry for *button*:

(11) a. buttonhole:
$[_N [_N$ button $][_N$ hole $]]$

b. buttonhook:
$[_N [_N$ button $][_N$ hook $]]$

c. button mushroom:
$[_N [_N$ button $][_N$ mushroom $]]$

In Spanish, for example, other types of compounds are equally important, including adjective-adjective compounds:

(12) a. guardacostas ('coastguard'):
$[_N [_N$ guarda $][_N$ costas $]]$

b. rojiblanco ('red and white'):
$[_A [_A$ roji $][_A$ blanco $]]$

Orthographically, different languages follow different conventions for compounds. For example, in German compounds are generally written as one word, but in English some are written as one word (as *buttonhole* and *buttonhook* above), some as hyphenated words (e.g. *small-scale*) and some as juxtaposed words (e.g. *button mushroom*).

As with derivations, it is possible to describe the range of possible compounds by means of a word grammar, and as with derivations the possibility that one might be able to translate compounds by translating the component parts is very attractive — especially since it is in principle not possible to list all English compounds, because compounding can give rise to words that are arbitrarily long. To see this, consider that one can form, in addition to *film society*:

(13) a. student film

b. student film society

c. student film society committee

d. student film society committee scandal

e. student film society committee scandal inquiry

Unfortunately, though there are cases where decomposing a compound and translating its parts gives correct results (e.g. the German compound *Wassersportverein* translates as *water sport club*), the problems of interpretation and translation are even worse for compounds than for derivations. Apart from the fact that some compounds have completely idiosyncratic interpretations (e.g. a *redhead* is a person with ginger coloured hair), there are problems of ambiguity. For example, *student film society* could have either of the structures indicated, with different interpretations (the first might denote a society for student films, the second a film society for students):[10]

(14) a. [*N* [*N* student film]society]

   b. [*N* student [*N* film society]]

A different type of ambiguity can be illustrated by giving an example: *satellite observation* may on one occasion of use mean *observation by satellite*, while on another occasion of use it might mean *observation of satellites*. Most of the time humans are able to rely on either our world knowledge or on the context to unravel a compound's meaning. Moreover, it is frequently important for translation purposes to work out the exact relation expressed by a compound. In Romance languages, for example, this relation may be explicitly realised by a preposition. For example, *research infrastructure* in Spanish translates as *infraestructura para la investigación* (literally, 'infrastructure *for* research'). Nor can we happily assume that an ambiguity in one language will be preserved in another. Thus *satellite observation* has two possible translations in Spanish, depending on its meaning: *observación por satelite* ('observation by satellite') and *observación de satelites* ('observation of satellites').

A further problem with compounds is that a wide variety of relations are possible between the elements of a compound. Thus *buttonhole* is a hole for buttons, but *button mushroom* is a mushroom that resembles a button. It is not clear how to capture these relations.

Thus, as with derivations, a really general approach to the treatment of compounds remains a research goal for MT.

5.5 Terminology

The discussion so far has been about issues relating to general vocabulary. However, a slightly different, and somewhat less troublesome, set of issues arise when

---

[10]Where words have been fused together to form a compound, as is prototypically the case in German, an additional problem presents itself in the analysis of the compound, namely to decide exactly which words the compound consists of. The German word *Wachtraum*, for example, could have been formed by joining *Wach* and *Traum* giving a composite meaning of *day-dream*. On the other hand, it could have been formed by joining *Wacht* to *Raum*, in which case the compound would mean *guard-room*.

one turns to the specialist vocabulary that one finds in certain types of text in certain subject fields (the vocabulary of weather reports is an extreme example, other examples might be the vocabulary of reports on trials for medical reports, reports of tests of pharmaceutical drugs, or reports of particular kinds of sporting event). Such fields often have a relatively well-defined terminology, which is sometimes even codified, and given official recognition by professional bodies. What this codification involves is settling on a collection of concepts, and assigning each a name (or perhaps several names, one in each of several languages). When a word (or collection of words in several languages) designate a single concept in this way, it is called a term. Examples of terms include the names for material objects, but also the abstract entities (processes, properties, functions, etc). Concepts, and hence the associated terms, can be organized into conceptual structures, based on the relationship between them. For example tables, chairs, cupboards, etc. can be grouped together as *furniture*, with a possible subdivision into *household furniture* and *office furniture*.

Terms may be simple words or multiword expressions. Syntactically, there is nothing to distinguish terms from ordinary language, although there is a strong tendency for terms to be nouns, often compound nouns.

Terms are potentially more tractable for MT systems than general language vocabulary, since for the most part they tend to be less ambiguous. While a general language word may represent more than one concept in a system of concepts, there is frequently a one-to-one mapping between terms and the concepts they represent. Take for example the word *graduation*, which in machine tool terminology has the very precise meaning: "distribution of divisions on the scale of an apparatus (linear, logarithmic, quadratic, etc)" The general language word *graduation*, on the other hand, has many more meanings, including "the ceremony at which degrees are conferred". What this means, of course, is that one can in principle adopt an interlingual approach to terminology. For example, even in a transfer system, one need not deal with terms on a language pair basis — all one may need is to have analysis and synthesis rules which relate the words for individual terms to an interlingual name for the associated concept (this could be an arbitrary numerical code, a collection of features, or even the actual term used in one of the languages, of course).

It is not always the case that a term represents one and only one concept — there are examples of terms which are ambiguous. For example, in machine tool terminology the term *screw* is defined as follows: "a machine thread whose essential element is a screw thread. A screw is either an external screw or an internal screw." (Likewise, synonymy amongst terms occurs, though much less frequent than in general language. In machine tool terminology, for example, *cramp* and *clamp* appear to designate the same concept.) However, the problems of ambiguity are small when compared to the problems one has with general vocabulary.

There are still some translational problems with terminology, however. In particular, there are problems whenever there is a mismatch between the conceptual systems of the two languages to be translated. An example of a concept mismatch from wine-making terminology is the difference between the English *acid* and the French *acide* which are defined as follows:

(15)   a.   **acid**: term applied to wine containing an excessive amount of $\boxed{\text{acid}}$, usually a wine made from grapes not completely ripe.

   b.   **acide**: caractère d'un vin dont la teneur elevée en $\boxed{\text{acides organiques}}$ provient généralement de raisins complètement mûrs.

While the French definition speaks of *acides organiques* ('organic acids'), the English speaks only of *acids*. If the mismatch is considered significant enough, the term may need to be paraphrased in the other language. In such cases translating terminology raises the same problems as dealing with general vocabulary.

Fortunately, problem cases in terminology translation are much less frequent than in general vocabulary.

From the point of view of the human translator, and more particularly, groups of human translators collaborating on the translation of documents, terminology poses other sorts of problem. First, there is the problem of size — the sheer number of terms there are to deal with. Second, there is the problem of consistency.

With respect to the second problem, MT offers a considerable advantage. This is because once a term has been translated, it is possible to store the term and its translation, and ensure that the term is translated consistently throughout texts.

Of course, this is partly a solution to the problem of size also, because it ensures that the research and effort that goes into finding a translation for a term is not duplicated by other translators working with the same system. However, it is only a partial solution, because there is a seemingly inexorable increase in terminology in many subject areas. Many hours of research are put into the recognition and documentation of new terms and their translational equivalents in other languages. To alleviate this problem, many translators and translation bureaux make use of **termbanks**, either pre-existing, or constructed in-house.

Termbanks are basically databases which contain many thousands of entries, one for every term. These entries consist, just like dictionary entries, of several fields, but the type of information given in these fields is rather different from that which one finds in an ordinary dictionary. Partly, this is because the proper documentation of a term requires specific information about the provenance of the entry, and about when it was created, and when modified (of course, one would expect to find information of this kind available to the builders of a properly documented dictionary too). Other information will typically concern related terms (synonyms, antonyms, abbreviations, superordinate terms and hyponyms), subject area (e.g.

pharmaceutical products vs. sports goods), and sources of further information (e.g. specialist dictionaries or reference books). On the other hand, information about grammatical properties and pronunciation is typically rather scant. This is partly because terms are very often new words, or loan words, and typically follow the regular morphological rules of a language. Similarly, the lack of phonological information is partly because the entries are oriented towards written material, but also because it is expected that the terms will be phonologically regular (i.e. they will follow the normal rules for the language, or the normal rules that apply to loans words).

Apart from in-house termbanks which are local to a single organization, there are a number of large termbanks which offer open access (sometimes at a small charge). Examples are *Eurodicautom* (European Commission), *Termium* (Canadian Government), *Normaterm* (the French standards organization) and *Frantext* (National Institute of the French Language), which offer a range of terminology areas including science, technology, administration, agriculture, medicine, law and economics.

It should be evident from even this brief discussion that ensuring clear and consistent use and translation of terminology is a significant factor in the translation process, which in most technical domains necessitates the creation and maintenance of termbanks — itself a costly and time-consuming endeavour. It is not surprising, therefore, that with the increasing availability of large amounts of on-line texts, researchers have begun to experiment with the automatic extraction of terms from running text, using a variety of statistical methods to determine the likelihood that a word, or string of words, constitutes a term. Of course, lists of (putative) terms cannot be made to emerge magically from a corpus of texts - the process takes into account the frequency of items in the texts and is often guided by some information provided by the user, such as a thesaurus of concepts or concept hierarchy or a list of already identified terms, or a list of typical syntactic patterns for terms. There is no reason to expect such techniques to be limited to the extraction of monolingual terminology, and in fact the idea of automating to some degree the compilation of bilingual and multilingual termbanks is also gaining ground.

5.6   Summary

This Chapter has dealt with a number of issues concerning dictionaries in MT, including issues relating to various kinds of word structure (morphology), and terminology. Apart from stressing their importance, we have outlined the main sorts of information that one typically finds in dictionaries, and raised some questions about how this information should be represented.

5.7   Further Reading

A readable account of what is involved in producing a dictionary can be found in [Sinclair, 1987] — in this case the dictionary is monolingual, and intended for human readers, but many of the issues are similar. A general discussion of what are taken to be the main theoretical issues in the design and construction of dictionaries for NLP purposes is given in [Ritchie, 1987].

On morphology, [Spencer, 1991] provides an excellent up-to-date description of current linguistic theory. For a more extensive discussion of compounding see [Bauer, 1983]. A detailed description of the state of the art as regards computational treatments of morphological phenomena is given in [Ritchie *et al.*, 1992]. Almost the only discussion of morphology which is specifically related to MT is [Bennett, 1993].

For a general introduction to the study of terminology, see [Sager, 1990], on termbanks, see [Bennett *et al.*, 1986; McNaught, 1988b; McNaught, forthcoming; McNaught, 1988a]. For discussion of computerized termbanks and translation, see [Thomas, 1992]. Experience of using a terminological database in the translation process is reported in [Paillet, 1990].

These days, many paper dictionaries exist in machine readable form (i.e. they have been created as 'electronic documents' in the sense of Chapter 8, below). OALD, the Oxford Advanced Learners' Dictionary [Hornby *et al.*, 1974], from which the monolingual entry on page 89 is taken, and LDOCE, Longman's Dictionary of Contemporary English [Proctor, 1978], are typical in this respect. They are sufficiently consistent and explicit to have been used in a number of experiments which try to take 'paper' dictionaries (or rather the machine readable versions of them), and convert them into a form which can be used directly in NLP systems. Some of this work is reported in [Boguraev and Briscoe, 1989].

The representation and use of lexical information in NLP is the focus of a great deal of research currently. Some idea of the range of this can be obtained from [Evens, 1988] and [Pustejovsky and Bergler, 1992]. The idea of structuring a dictionary hierarchically so that individual entries can inherit information (and so be simplified), which we mentioned briefly, is particularly important in this research. A clearer idea of what is involved can be gained from [Pollard and Sag, 1987, Chapter 8].

Chapter 6

Translation Problems

6.1 Introduction

In this chapter we will consider some particular problems which the task of translation poses for the builder of MT systems — some of the reasons why MT is hard. It is useful to think of these problems under two headings: (i) Problems of *ambiguity*, (ii) problems that arise from *structural* and *lexical differences* between languages and (iii) multiword units like idioms and collocations. We will discuss typical problems of ambiguity in Section 6.2, lexical and structural mismatches in Section 6.3, and multiword units in Section 6.4.

Of course, these sorts of problem are not the only reasons why MT is hard. Other problems include the sheer size of the undertaking, as indicated by the number of rules and dictionary entries that a realistic system will need, and the fact that there are many constructions whose grammar is poorly understood, in the sense that it is not clear how they should be represented, or what rules should be used to describe them. This is the case even for English, which has been extensively studied, and for which there are detailed descriptions – both traditional 'descriptive' and theoretically sophisticated – some of which are written with computational usability in mind. It is an even worse problem for other languages. Moreover, even where there is a reasonable description of a phenomenon or construction, producing a description which is sufficiently precise to be used by an automatic system raises non-trivial problems.

6.2 Ambiguity

In the best of all possible worlds (as far as most Natural Language Processing is concerned, anyway) every word would have one and only one meaning. But, as we all know, this is not the case. When a word has more than one meaning, it is said to be **lexically ambiguous**. When a phrase or sentence can have more than one structure it is said to be **structurally ambiguous**.

Ambiguity is a pervasive phenomenon in human languages. It is very hard to find words that are not at least two ways ambiguous, and sentences which are (out of context) several ways ambiguous are the rule, not the exception. This is not only problematic because some of the alternatives are unintended (i.e. represent wrong interpretations), but because ambiguities 'multiply'. In the worst case, a sentence containing two words, each of which is two ways ambiguous may be four ways ambiguous (2×2), one with three such words may be $2 \times 2 \times 2 = 2^3 = 8$, ways ambiguous etc. One can, in this way, get very large numbers indeed. For example, a sentence consisting of ten words, each two ways ambiguous, and with just two possible structural analyses could have $2^{9+2} = 2^{11} = 2048$ different analyses. The number of analyses can be problematic, since one may have to consider all of them, rejecting all but one.

Fortunately, however, things are not always so bad. In the rest of this section we will look at the problem in more detail, and consider some partial solutions.

Imagine that we are trying to translate these two sentences into French:

(1)   a.   You must not $\boxed{\text{use}}$ abrasive cleaners on the printer casing.

   b.   The $\boxed{\text{use}}$ of abrasive cleaners on the printer casing is not recommended.

In the first sentence *use* is a verb, and in the second a noun, that is, we have a case of lexical ambiguity. An English-French dictionary will say that the verb can be translated by (inter alia) *se servir de* and *employer*, whereas the noun is translated as *emploi* or *utilisation*. One way a reader or an automatic parser can find out whether the noun or verb form of *use* is being employed in a sentence is by working out whether it is grammatically possible to have a noun or a verb in the place where it occurs. For example, in English, there is no grammatical sequence of words which consists of *the* + V + PP — so of the two possible parts of speech to which *use* can belong, only the noun is possible in the second sentence (1b).

As we have noted in Chapter 4, we can give translation engines such information about grammar, in the form of grammar rules. This is useful in that it allows them to filter out some wrong analyses. However, giving our system knowledge about syntax will not allow us to determine the meaning of all ambiguous words. This is because words can have several meanings even within the same part of speech. Take for example the word *button*.Like the word *use*, it can be either a verb or a noun. As a noun, it can mean both the familiar small round object used to fasten clothes, as well as a knob on a piece of apparatus. To get the machine to pick out the right interpretation we have to give it information about meaning.

In fact, arming a computer with knowledge about syntax, without at the same time telling it something about meaning can be a dangerous thing. This is because applying a grammar to a sentence can produce a number of different analyses, depending on how the rules have applied, and we may end up with a large number of alternative analyses for a single sentence. Now syntactic ambiguity may coincide with genuine meaning ambiguity, but very often it does not, and it is the cases where it does not that we want to eliminate by applying knowledge about meaning.

We can illustrate this with some examples. First, let us show how grammar rules, differently applied, can produce more than one syntactic analysis for a sentence. One way this can occur is where a word is assigned to more than one category in the grammar. For example, assume that the word *cleaning* is both an adjective and a verb in our grammar. This will allow us to assign two different analyses to the following sentence.

(2)   Cleaning fluids can be dangerous.

One of these analyses will have *cleaning* as a verb, and one will have it as an adjective. In the former (less plausible) case the sense is 'to clean a fluid may be dangerous', i.e. it is about an activity being dangerous. In the latter case the sense is that fluids used for cleaning can be dangerous. Choosing between these alternative syntactic analyses requires knowledge about meaning.

It may be worth noting, in passing, that this ambiguity disappears when *can* is replaced by a verb which shows number agreement by having different forms for third person singular and plural. For example, the following are not ambiguous in this way: (3a) has only the sense that the action is dangerous, (3b) has only the sense that the fluids are dangerous.

(3)   a.   Cleaning fluids is dangerous.
      b.   Cleaning fluids are dangerous.

We have seen that syntactic analysis is useful in ruling out some wrong analyses, and this is another such case, since, by checking for agreement of subject and object, it is possible to find the correct interpretations. A system which ignored such syntactic facts would have to consider all these examples ambiguous, and would have to find some other way of working out which sense was intended, running the risk of making the wrong choice. For a system with proper syntactic analysis, this problem would arise only in the case of verbs like *can* which do not show number agreement.

Another source of syntactic ambiguity is where whole phrases, typically prepositional phrases, can attach to more than one position in a sentence. For example, in the following example, the prepositional phrase *with a Postscript interface* can attach either to the NP *the word processor package*, meaning "the word-processor which is fitted or supplied with a Postscript interface", or to the verb *connect*, in which case the sense is that the Postscript interface is to be used to make the connection.

(4)   Connect the printer to a word processor package with a Postscript interface.

Notice, however, that this example is not genuinely ambiguous at all, knowledge of what a Postscript interface is (in particular, the fact that it is a piece of software, not a piece of hardware that could be used for making a physical connection between a printer to an office computer) serves to disambiguate. Similar problems arise with (5), which could mean that the printer and the word processor both need Postscript interfaces, or that only the word processor needs them.

(5)   You will require a printer and a word processor with Postscript interfaces.

This kind of real world knowledge is also an essential component in disambiguating the pronoun *it* in examples such as the following

(6)   Put the paper in the printer. Then switch it on.

In order to work out that *it* is the printer that is to be switched on, rather than the paper, one needs to use the knowledge of the world that printers (and not paper) are the sort of thing one is likely to switch on.

There are other cases where real world knowledge, though necessary, does not seem to be sufficient. The following, where two people are re-assembling a printer, seems to be such an example:

(7)   A: Now insert the cartridge at the back.
        B: Okay.
        A: By the way, did you order more toner today?
        B: Yes, I got some when I picked up the new paper.
        A: OK, how far have you got?
           Did you get ⬚it⬚ fixed?

It is not clear that any kind of real world knowledge will be enough to work out that *it* in the last sentence refers to the cartridge, rather than the new paper, or toner. All are probably equally reasonable candidates for fixing. What strongly suggests that *it* should be interpreted as the cartridge is the structure of the conversation — the discussion of the toner and new paper occurs in a digression, which has ended by the time *it* occurs. Here what one needs is knowledge of the way language is used. This is knowledge which is usually thought of as pragmatic in nature. Analysing the meaning of texts like the above example is important in dialogue translation, which is a long term goal for MT research, but similar problems occur in other sorts of text.

Another sort of pragmatic knowledge is involved in cases where the translation of a sentence depends on the communicative intention of the speaker — on the sort of action (the speech act) that the speaker intends to perform with the sentence. For example, (8) could be a request for action, or a request for information, and this might make a difference to the translation.

(8)   Can you reprogram the printer interface on this printer?

In some cases, working out which is intended will depend on the non-linguistic situation, but it could also depend on the kind of discourse that is going on — for example, is it a discourse where requests for action are expected, and is the speaker in a position to make such a request of the hearer? In dialogues, such pragmatic information about the discourse can be important for translating the simplest expressions. For example, the right translation of *Thank you* into French depends on what sort of speech act it follows. Normally, one would expect the translation to be *merci*. However, if it is uttered in response to an offer, the right translation would be *s'il vous plaît* ('please').

6.3   Lexical and Structural Mismatches

At the start of the previous section we said that, in the best of all possible worlds for NLP, every word would have exactly one sense. While this is true for most NLP, it is an exaggeration as regards MT. It would be a *better* world, but not the best of all possible worlds, because we would still be faced with difficult translation problems. Some of these problems are to do with lexical differences between languages — differences in the ways in which languages seem to classify the world, what concepts they choose to express by single words, and which they choose not to lexicalize. We will look at some of these directly. Other problems arise because different languages use different structures for the same purpose, and the same structure for different purposes. In either case, the result is that we have to complicate the translation process. In this section we will look at some representative examples.

Examples like the ones in (9) below are familiar to translators, but the examples of colours (9c), and the Japanese examples in (9d) are particularly striking. The latter because they show how languages need differ not only with respect to the fineness or 'granularity' of the distinctions they make, but also with respect to the basis for the distinction: English chooses different verbs for the action/event of putting on, and the action/state of wearing. Japanese does not make this distinction, but differentiates according to the object that is worn. In the case of English to Japanese, a fairly simple test on the semantics of the NPs that accompany a verb may be sufficient to decide on the right translation. Some of the colour examples are similar, but more generally, investigation of colour vocabulary indicates that languages actually carve up the spectrum in rather different ways, and that deciding on the best translation may require knowledge that goes well beyond what is in the text, and may even be undecidable. In this sense, the translation of colour terminology begins to resemble the translation of terms for cultural artifacts (e.g. words like English *cottage*, Russian *dacha*, French *château*, etc. for which no adequate translation exists, and for which the human translator must decide between straight borrowing, neologism, and providing an explanation). In this area, translation is a genuinely creative act[1], which is well beyond the capacity of current computers.

(9) a. know (V)   savoir (a fact)
                            connaître (a thing)
      b. leg (N)   patte (of an animal)
                            jambe (of a human)
                            pied (of a table)
      c. brown (A)   brun
                            châtain (of hair)
                            marron (of shoes/leather)
      d. wear/put on (V)   kiku
                            haku (shoes)
                            kakeru (glasses)
                            kaburu (hats)
                            hameru (gloves, etc. i.e. on hands)
                            haoru (coat)
                            shimeru (scarves, etc. i.e. round the neck)

Calling cases such as those above lexical mismatches is not controversial. However, when one turns to cases of structural mismatch, classification is not so easy. This is because one may often think that the reason one language uses one construction, where another uses another is because of the stock of lexical items the two languages have. Thus, the distinction is to some extent a matter of taste and convenience.

A particularly obvious example of this involves problems arising from what are sometimes called **lexical holes** — that is, cases where one language has to use a phrase to express what another language expresses in a single word. Examples of this include the 'hole' that exists in English with respect to French *ignorer* ('to not know', 'to be ignorant of'), and *se suicider* ('to suicide', i.e. 'to commit suicide', 'to kill oneself'). The problems raised by such lexical holes have a certain similarity to those raised by idioms: in both cases, one has phrases translating as single words. We will therefore postpone discussion of these until Section 6.4.

---

[1]Creative in the sense of 'genuine invention which is not governed by rules', rather than the sense of 'creating new things by following rules' — computers have no problem with creating new things by following rules, of course.

One kind of structural mismatch occurs where two languages use the same construction for different purposes, or use different constructions for what appears to be the same purpose.

Cases where the same structure is used for different purposes include the use of passive constructions in English, and Japanese. In the example below, the Japanese particle *wa*, which we have glossed as 'TOP' here marks the 'topic' of the sentence — intuitively, what the sentence is about.

(10) a. Satoo-san wa shyushoo ni erabaremashita.
    Satoo-hon TOP Prime Minister in was-elected

   b. Mr. Satoh was elected Prime Minister.

Example (10) indicates that Japanese has a passive-like construction, i.e. a construction where the PATIENT, which is normally realized as an OBJECT, is realized as SUBJECT. It is different from the English passive in the sense that in Japanese this construction tends to have an extra adversive nuance which might make (10a) rather odd, since it suggests an interpretation where Mr Satoh did not want to be elected, or where election is somehow bad for him. This is not suggested by the English translation, of course. The translation problem from Japanese to English is one of those that looks unsolvable for MT, though one might try to convey the intended sense by adding an adverb such as *unfortunately*. The translation problem from English to Japanese is on the other hand within the scope of MT, since one must just choose another form. This is possible, since Japanese allows SUBJECTs to be omitted freely, so one can say the equivalent of *elected Mr Satoh*, and thus avoid having to mention an AGENT [2]. However, in general, the result of this is that one cannot have simple rules like those described in Chapter 4 for passives. In fact, unless one uses a very abstract structure indeed, the rules will be rather complicated.

We can see different constructions used for the same effect in cases like the following:

(11) a. He is called Sam.

   b. Er heißt Sam.
    'He is-named Sam'

   c. Il s'appelle Sam.
    'He calls himself Sam'

(12) a. Sam has just seen Kim.

---

[2]This discussion of the Japanese passive is a slight simplification. The construction does sometimes occur without the adversive sense, but this is usually regarded as a 'europeanism', showing the influence of European languages.

    b. Sam vient de voir Kim.
        'Sam comes of see Kim'

(13) a. Sam likes to swim.

      b. Sam zwemt graag.
          'Sam swims likingly'

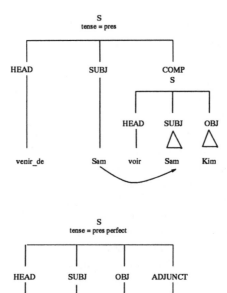

Figure 6.1 *venir-de* and *have-just*

The first example shows how English, German and French choose different methods for expressing 'naming'. The other two examples show one language using an adverbial ADJUNCT (*just*, or *graag*(Dutch) 'likingly' or 'with pleasure'), where another uses a verbal construction. This is actually one of the most discussed problems in current MT, and it is worth examining why it is problematic. This can be seen by looking at the representations for (12) in Figure 6.1.

These representations are relatively abstract (e.g. the information about tense and aspect conveyed by the auxiliary verb *have* has been expressed in a feature), but they are still rather different. In particular, notice that while the main verb of (12a) is *see*, the main verb of (12b) is *venir-de*. Now notice what is involved in writing rules which relate these structures (we will look at the direction English → French).

1 The adverb *just* must be translated as the verb *venir-de* (perhaps this is not the best way to think about it — the point is that the French structure must contain *venir-de*, and *just* must not be translated in any other way).

2 *Sam*, the SUBJECT of *see*, must become the SUBJECT of *venir-de*.

3 Some information about tense, etc. must be taken from the S node of which *see* is the HEAD, and put on the S node of which *venir-de* is the HEAD. This is a complication, because normally one would expect such information to go on the node of which the translation of *see*, *voir*, is the HEAD.

4 Other parts of the English sentence should go into the corresponding parts of the sentence HEADed by *voir*. This is simple enough here, because in both cases *Kim* is an OBJECT, but it is not always the case that OBJECTs translate as OBJECTs, of course.

5 The link between the SUBJECT of *venir-de* and the SUBJECT of *voir* must be established — but this can perhaps be left to French synthesis.

All this is summarized in Figure 6.2 and Figure 6.3.

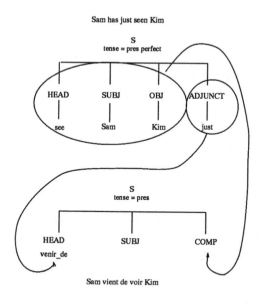

Figure 6.2 Translating *have-just* into *venir-de*

Of course, given a complicated enough rule, all this can be stated. However, there will still be problems because writing a rule in isolation is not enough. One must also consider how the rule interacts with other rules. For example, there will be a rule somewhere that tells the system how *see* is to be translated, and what one should do with its SUBJECT and OBJECT. One must make sure that this rule still works (e.g. its application is not blocked by the fact that the SUBJECT is dealt with by the special rule above; or that it does not insert an extra SUBJECT into the translation, which would give *Sam vient de Sam voir Kim). One must also make sure that the rule works when there are other problematic phenomena around. For example, one might like to make sure the system produces (14b) as the translation of (14a).

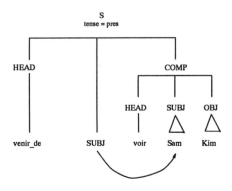

Figure 6.3 The Representation of *venir-de*

(14)   a.   Sam has probably just seen Kim.

     b.   Il est probable que Sam vient de voir Kim.
        'It is probable that Sam comes of see Kim'

We said above that everything except the SUBJECT, and some of the tense information goes into the 'lower' sentence in French. But this is clearly not true, since here the translation of *probably* actually becomes part of the main sentence, with the translation of (12a) as its COMPLEMENT.

Of course, one could try to argue that the difference between English *just* and French *venir de* is only superficial. The argument could, for example, say that *just* should be treated as a verb at the semantic level. However, this is not very plausible. There are other cases where this does not seem possible. Examples like the following show that where English uses a 'manner' verb and a directional adverb/prepositional phrase, French (and other Romance languages) use a directional verb and a manner adverb. That is where English classifies the event described as 'running', French classifies it as an 'entering':

(15)   a.   She ran into the room.

     b.   Elle entra dans la salle en courant.
        'She entered into the room in/while running'

The syntactic structures of these examples are very different, and it is hard to see how one can naturally reduce them to similar structures without using very abstract representations indeed.

A slightly different sort of structural mismatch occurs where two languages have 'the same' construction (more precisely, similar constructions, with equivalent interpretations), but where different restrictions on the constructions mean that it is not always possible to translate in the most obvious way. The following is a relatively simple example of this.

(16) a.   These are the letters which I have already replied to.

  b.   *Ce sont les lettres lesquelles j'ai déjà répondu à.

  c.   These are the letters to which I have already replied.

  d.   Ce sont les lettres auxquelles j'ai déjà répondu.

What this shows is that English and French differ in that English permits prepositions to be 'stranded' (i.e. to appear without their objects, like in 16a). French normally requires the preposition and its object to appear together, as in (16d) — of course, English allows this too. This will make translating (16a) into French difficult for many sorts of system (in particular, for systems that try to manage without fairly abstract syntactic representations). However, the general solution is fairly clear — what one wants is to build a structure where (16a) is represented in the same way as (16c), since this will eliminate the translation problem. The most obvious representation would probably be something along the lines of (17a), or perhaps (17b).

(17) a.   These are the letters [$_S$ I have already replied [$_{PP}$ to which]]

  b.   These are the letters [$_S$ I have already replied [$_{PP}$ to the letters]]

While by no means a complete solution to the treatment of relative clause constructions, such an approach probably overcomes this particular translation problem. There are other cases which pose worse problems, however.

In general, relative clause constructions in English consist of a head noun (*letters* in the previous example), a relative pronoun (such as *which*), and a sentence with a 'gap' in it. The relative pronoun (and hence the head noun) is understood as if it filled the gap — this is the idea behind the representations in (17). In English, there are restrictions on where the 'gap' can occur. In particular, it cannot occur inside an indirect question, or a 'reason' ADJUNCT. Thus, (18b), and (18d) are both ungrammatical. However, these restrictions are not exactly paralleled in other languages. For example, Italian allows the former, as in (18a), and Japanese the latter, as in (18c). These sorts of problem are beyond the scope of current MT systems — in fact, they are difficult even for human translators.

(18) a.   Sinda node minna ga kanasinda hito wa yumei desita.
           'died hence everyone SUBJ distressed-was man TOP famous was'

      b.   *The man who everyone was distressed because (he) died was famous.

      c.   L'uomo che mi domando chi abbia visto fu arrestato.

      d.   *The man that I wonder who (he) has seen was arrested.

6.4   Multiword units: Idioms and Collocations

Roughly speaking, **idioms** are expressions whose meaning cannot be completely understood from the meanings of the component parts. For example, whereas it is possible to work out the meaning of (19a) on the basis of knowledge of English grammar and the meaning of words, this would not be sufficient to work out that (19b) can mean something like 'If Sam dies, her children will be rich'. This is because *kick the bucket* is an idiom.

(19) a.   If Sam mends the bucket, her children will be rich.

      b.   If Sam kicks the bucket, her children will be rich.

The problem with idioms, in an MT context, is that it is not usually possible to translate them using the normal rules. There are exceptions, for example *take the bull by the horns* (meaning 'face and tackle a difficulty without shirking') can be translated literally into French as *prendre le taureau par les cornes*, which has the same meaning. But, for the most part, the use of normal rules in order to translate idioms will result in nonsense. Instead, one has to treat idioms as single units in translation.

In many cases, a natural translation for an idiom will be a single word — for example, the French word *mourir* ('die') is a possible translation for *kick the bucket*. This brings out the similarity, which we noted above, with lexical holes of the kind shown in (20).

(20) a.   J'ignore la solution.

      b.   I do not know the solution.

      c.   se suicider.

      d.   commit suicide.

Lexical holes and idioms are frequently instances of word ↔ phrase translation. The difference is that with lexical holes, the problem typically arises when one translates from the language with the word into the language that uses the phrase, whereas with idioms, one usually gets the problem in translating from the language that has the idiom (i.e. the phrase) into the language which uses a single word. For example, there is no problem in translating *I do not know the solution* literally into French — the result is perfectly understandable. Similarly, there is no problem in translating *mourir* 'literally' into English (as *die*) — one is not forced to use the idiom *kick the bucket*.

In general, there are two approaches one can take to the treatment of idioms. The first is to try to represent them as single units in the monolingual dictionaries. What this means is that one will have lexical entries such as `kick_the_bucket`. One might try to construct special morphological rules to produce these representations before performing any syntactic analysis — this would amount to treating idioms as a special kind of word, which just happens to have spaces in it. As will become clear, this is not a workable solution in general. A more reasonable idea is not to regard lexical lookup as a single process that occurs just once, before any syntactic or semantic processing, but to allow analysis rules to replace pieces of structure by information which is held in the lexicon at different stages of processing, just as they are allowed to change structures in other ways. This would mean that *kick the bucket* and the non-idiomatic *kick the table* would be represented alike (apart from the difference between *bucket* and *table*) at one level of analysis, but that at a later, more abstract representation *kick the bucket* would be replaced with a single node, with the information at this node coming from the lexical entry `kick_the_bucket`. This information would probably be similar to the information one would find in the entry for *die*.

In any event, this approach will lead to translation rules saying something like the following, in a transformer or transfer system (in an interlingual system, idioms will correspond to collections of concepts, or single concepts in the same way as normal words).

```
in_fact => en_fait

in_view_of => étant_donné

kick_the_bucket => mourir

kick_the_bucket => casser_sa_pipe
```

The final example shows that one might, in this way, be able to translate the idiom *kick the bucket* into the equivalent French idiom *casser sa pipe* — literally 'break his/her pipe'. The overall translation process is illustrated in Figure 6.4.

The second approach to idioms is to treat them with special rules that change the idiomatic source structure into an appropriate target structure. This would mean that *kick the bucket* and *kick the table* would have similar representations all through analysis. Clearly, this approach is only applicable in transfer or transformer systems, and even here, it is not very different from the first approach — in the case where an idiom translates as a single word, it is simply a question of where one carries out the replacement of a structure by a single lexical item, and whether the item in question is an abstract source language word such as *kick_the_bucket* or a normal target language word (such as *mourir*).

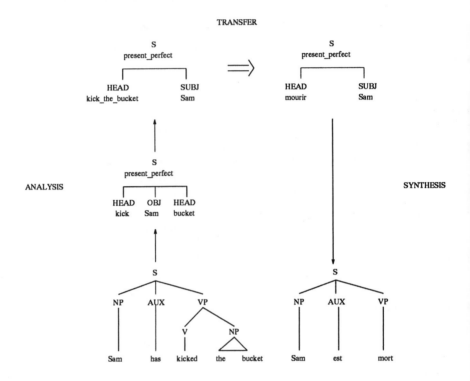

Figure 6.4 Dealing with Idioms 1

One problem with sentences which contain idioms is that they are typically ambiguous, in the sense that either a literal or idiomatic interpretation is generally possible (i.e. the phrase *kick the bucket* can really be about buckets and kicking). However, the possibility of having a variety of interpretations does not really distinguish them from other sorts of expression. Another problem is that they need special rules (such as those above, perhaps), in addition to the normal rules for ordinary words and constructions. However, in this they are no different from ordinary words, for which one also needs special rules. The real problem with idioms is that they are not generally fixed in their form, and that the variation of forms is not limited to variations in inflection (as it is with ordinary words). Thus, there is a serious problem in recognising idioms.

This problem does not arise with all idioms. Some are completely frozen forms whose parts always appear in the same form and in the same order. Examples are phrases like *in fact*, or *in view of*. However, such idioms are by far the exception. A typical way in which idioms can vary is in the form of the verb, which changes according to tense, as well as person and number. For example, with *bury the hatchet* ('to cease hostilities and becomes reconciled', one gets *He buries/buried/will bury the hatchet*, and *They bury/buried/shall bury the hatchet*. Notice that variation in the form one gets here is exactly what one would get if no idiomatic interpretation was involved — i.e. by and large idioms are syntactically and morphologically regular — it is only their interpretations that are surprising.

A second common form of variation is in the form of the possessive pronoun in expressions like *to burn one's bridges* (meaning 'to proceed in such a way as to eliminate all alternative courses of action'). This varies in a regular way with the subject of the verb:

(21) a. He has burned his bridges.

   b. She has burned her bridges.

In other cases, only the syntactic category of an element in an idiom can be predicted. Thus, the idiom *pull X's leg* ('tease') contains a genitive NP, such as *Sam's*, or *the king of England's*. Another common form of variation arises because some idioms allow adjectival modifiers. Thus in addition to *keep tabs on* (meaning *observe*) one has *keep **close** tabs on* ('observe closely'), or *put a **political** cat among the pigeons* (meaning 'do or say something that causes a lot of argument politically'). Some idioms appear in different syntactic configurations, just like regular non-idiomatic expressions. Thus, *bury the hatchet* appears in the passive, as well as the active voice.

(22) a. He buried the hatchet

   b. The hatchet seems to have been buried

Of course, not all idioms allow these variations (e.g. one cannot passivize *kick the bucket* meaning 'die'), and, as noted, some do not allow any variation in form. But where variation in form is allowed, there is clearly a problem. In particular, notice that it will not be possible to recognise idioms simply by looking for sequences of particular words in the input. Recognising some of these idioms will require a rather detailed syntactic analysis. For example, despite the variation in form for *bury the hatchet*, the idiomatic interpretation only occurs when *the hatchet* is always DEEP OBJECT of *bury*. Moreover, the rules that translate idioms or which replace them by single lexical items may have to be rather complex. Some idea of this can be gained from considering what must happen to *pull Sam's leg* in order to produce something like equivalent to *tease Sam*, or the French translation involving *taquiner* ('tease'), cf. Figure 6.5. This figure assumes the input and output of transfer are representations of grammatical relations, but the principles are the same if semantic representations are involved, or if the process involves reducing *pull X's leg* to a single word occurs in English analysis.

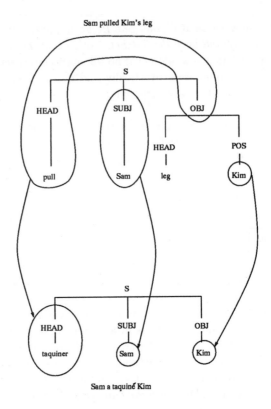

Figure 6.5 Dealing with Idioms 2

Rather different from idioms are expressions like those in (23), which are usually referred to as **collocations**. Here the meaning can be guessed from the meanings of the parts. What is not predictable is the particular words that are used.

(23) a.   This butter is rancid (*sour, *rotten, *stale).

  b.   This cream is sour (*rancid, *rotten, *stale).

  c.   They took (*made) a walk.

  d.   They made (*took) an attempt.

  e.   They had (*made, *took) a talk.

For example, the fact that we say *rancid* butter, but not *sour butter*, and *sour cream*, but not *rancid cream* does not seem to be completely predictable from the meaning of *butter* or *cream*, and the various adjectives. Similarly the choice of *take* as the verb for *walk* is not simply a matter of the meaning of *walk* (for example, one can either *make* or *take* a journey).

In what we have called linguistic knowledge (LK) systems, at least, collocations can potentially be treated differently from idioms. This is because for collocations one can often think of one part of the expression as being dependent on, and predictable from the other. For example, one may think that *make*, in *make an attempt* has little meaning of its own, and serves merely to 'support' the noun (such verbs are often called **light verbs**, or **support verbs**). This suggests one can simply ignore the verb in translation, and have the generation or synthesis component supply the appropriate verb. For example, in Dutch, this would be *doen*, since the Dutch for *make an attempt* is *een poging doen* ('do an attempt').

One way of doing this is to have analysis replace the lexical verb (e.g. *make*) with a 'dummy verb' (e.g. VSUP). This can be treated as a sort of interlingual lexical item, and replaced by the appropriate verb in synthesis (the identity of the appropriate verb has to be included in the lexical entry of nouns, of course — for example, the entry for *poging* might include the feature support_verb=doen. The advantage is that support verb constructions can be handled without recourse to the sort of rules required for idioms (one also avoids having rules that appear to translate *make* into *poging* 'do').

Of course, what one is doing here is simply recording, in each lexical entry, the identity of the words that are associated with it, for various purposes — e.g. the fact that the verb that goes with *attempt* is *make* (for some purposes, anyway). An interesting generalisation of this is found in the idea of **lexical functions**. Lexical functions express a relation between two words. Take the case of *heavy smoker*, for example. The relationship between *heavy* and *smoker* is that of intensification, which could be expressed by the lexical function Magn as follows, indicating that the appropriate adjective for English *smoker* is *heavy*, whereas that for the corresponding French word *fumeur* is *grand* ('large') and that for the German word *Raucher* is *stark* ('strong').

```
(English) Magn(smoker) = heavy

(French) Magn(fumeur) = grand

(German) Magn(Raucher) = stark
```

If one wants to translate *heavy smoker* into French, one needs to map *smoker* into *fumeur*, together with the information that *fumeur* has the lexical function Magn applied to it, as in English. It would be left to the French synthesis module to work out that the value Magn(fumeur) = *grand*, and insert this adjective appropriately. Translation into German is done in the same way.

6.5 Summary

This chapter looks at some problems which face the builder of MT systems. We characterized them as problems of ambiguity (lexical and syntactic) and problems of lexical and structural mismatches. We saw how different types of linguistic and non-linguistic knowledge are necessary to resolve problems of ambiguity, and in the next chapter we examine in more detail how to represent this knowledge. In this chapter we discussed instances of lexical and structural mismatches and the problem of non-compositionality (as exemplified by idioms and collocations) and looked at some strategies for dealing with them in MT systems.

6.6   Further Reading

The problem of ambiguity is pervasive in NLP, and is discussed extensively in the introductions to the subject such as those mentioned in the Further Reading section of Chapter 3.

Examples of lexical and structural mismatches are discussed in [Hutchins and Somers, 1992, Chapter 6]. Problems of the *venir-de/have just* sort are discussed extensively in the MT literature. A detailed discussion of the problem can be found in [Arnold *et al.*, 1988], and in [Sadler, 1993]. On light verbs or support verbs, see [Danlos and Samvelian, 1992; Danlos, 1992].

Treatments of idioms in MT are given in [Arnold and Sadler, 1989], and [Schenk, 1986]. On collocations, see for example [Allerton, 1984], [Benson *et al.*, 1986a], [Benson *et al.*, 1986b] and [Hanks and Church, 1989].   The notion of **lexical functions** is due to Mel'čuk, see for example [Mel'čuk and Polguere, 1987; Mel'čuk and Zholkovsky, 1988].

A classic discussion of translation problems is [Vinay and Darbelnet, 1977].   This is concerned with translation problems as faced by humans, rather than machines, but it points out several of the problems mentioned here.

The discussion in this chapter touches on two issues of general linguistic and philo-sophical interest: to what extent human languages really do carve the world up differently, and whether there are some sentences in some languages which cannot be translated into other languages. As regards the first question, it seems as though there are some limits. For example, though languages carve the colour spectrum up rather differently, so there can be rather large differences between colour words in terms of their extensions, there seems to be a high level of agreement about 'best instances'. That is, though the extension of English *red*, and Japanese *akai* is differ-ent, nevertheless, the colour which is regarded as the best instance of *red* by English speakers is the colour which is regarded as the best instance of *akai* by Japanese speakers. The seminal work on this topic is [Berlin and Kay, 1969], and see the title essay of [Pullum, 1991]. The second question is sometimes referred to as the question of **effability**, see [Katz, 1978; Keenan, 1978] for relevant discussion.

Chapter 7

Representation and Processing Revisited: Meaning

7.1 Introduction

The discussion in previous chapters reinforces the point made in Chapter 3 about the value of syntactic, and 'shallow' semantic analysis, but it also shows why performing a syntactic analysis alone is not sufficient for translation. As the discussion in Chapter 6 indicates, there are many cases where problems seem to require deeper, more meaning oriented representations, and enrichment of the kind of knowledge systems are equipped with. In this chapter we will try to give a flavour of what is involved in this.

It is useful to think of this knowledge as being of three kinds: (i) linguistic knowledge which is independent of context, semantic knowledge; (ii) linguistic knowledge which relates to the context (e.g. of earlier utterances), sometimes called pragmatic knowledge; and (iii) common sense, general, non-linguistic knowledge about the real world, which we will call real world knowledge. It should be stressed that the distinction between these different kinds of knowledge is not always clear, and there are those who would dispute whether the distinction is real. However, it is at least a convenient subdivision of the field, and we will examine each sort of knowledge in turn, in Sections 7.2, 7.3, and 7.4. Discussing these different kinds of knowledge will also allow us to describe some more general translation problems.

Apart from giving an overview and flavour of what is involved, the point we would like to stress in this chapter is that though dealing with meaning in a general way poses many unsolved problems, and in general one should not expect to find much in the way of real world, pragmatic, or even semantic processing in current commercial MT systems, such processing it is not *totally* beyond the reach of current theory.

7.2   Semantics

Semantics is concerned with the meaning of words and how they combine to form sentence meanings. It is useful to distinguish **lexical** semantics, and **structural** semantics — the former is to do with the meanings of words, the latter to do with the meanings of phrases, including sentences. We will begin with the former.

There are many ways of thinking about and representing word meanings, but one that has proved useful in the field of machine translation involves associating words with **semantic features** which correspond to their sense components. For example, the words *man, woman, boy*, and *girl* might be represented as:

```
man = (+HUMAN, +MASCULINE and +ADULT)

woman = (+HUMAN, -MASCULINE and +ADULT)

boy = (+HUMAN, +MASCULINE and -ADULT)

girl = (+HUMAN, -MASCULINE and -ADULT)
```

Associating words with semantic features is useful because some words impose semantic constraints on what other kinds of words they can occur with. For example, the verb *eat* demands that its AGENT (the eater) is animate and that its PATIENT (that which is eaten) is edible, — concrete (rather than abstract, like sincerity, or beauty), and solid (rather than liquid, so one cannot 'eat' beer, coffee, etc.; soup is a borderline case). We can encode this constraint in our grammar by associating the features HUMAN and EDIBLE with appropriate nouns in our dictionary and describing our entry for *eat* as something like cat=verb, AGENT=HUMAN, PATIENT=EDIBLE. The grammar will now only accept objects of *eat* that have the feature EDIBLE. Thus these **selectional restrictions**, as they are called, act as a filter on our grammar to rule out unwanted analyses. Consider sentence (1):

(1)   John ate the game.

The English word *game* is ambiguous - it can mean several things, including *a form of play or sport* or *a wild animal hunted or fished for food*. Using selectional restrictions of the sort described above we can eliminate the 'form of play or sport' meaning if the system is able to infer that 'food' is EDIBLE, but that forms of play are not.

Selectional restrictions have proved a very useful device and are found in most MT systems to a greater or lesser extent. Unfortunately, however, exceptions to selectional restrictions abound, especially in metaphorical speech. Thus we find sentences like *This car eats money*, used to mean that the car is expensive to maintain, so, rather than use selectional restrictions to eliminate interpretations, we should use them to state **preferences** between alternative interpretations.

Notice that stating selectional restrictions in terms of semantic relations is easier than trying to state them in terms of (surface) grammatical relations. Using grammatical relations we would have to say that *eat* prefers an animate SUBJECT in active sentences, and an animate NP in the *by* phrase in passive sentences (and an edible OBJECT in actives, and an edible SUBJECT in passives).

We will now look briefly at how semantic relations can help in one of the thorniest problems for machine translation, namely the translation of prepositions.

Take, for example, the translation of the English preposition *at* into Spanish, and, for the sake of exposition, make the simplifying assumption that it receives only two translations in Spanish, namely *a* and *en*, as in the following:

(2) a.   at midday

    b. $\boxed{\text{a}}$ mediodía

(3) a.   at school

    b. $\boxed{\text{en}}$ la escuela

The choice of Spanish preposition depends on the type of noun that follows it. Roughly, where the preposition is followed by a temporal noun, as in the first example, it translates as *a*, but where the preposition is followed by a locational noun, as in the second example, it translates as *en*.

We can pick out the correct translation of *at* by assigning it an appropriate Semantic Relation (SR) during analysis. For example, the feature SR=TIME might be assigned to indicate that *at* expresses a temporal relation, and the feature SR=PLACE might be used to mean that *at* expresses a location relation. We could then have translation rules of the following form:

    at, SR=TIME ↔ a

    at, SR=PLACE ↔ en

These semantic relations are assigned on the basis of the type of noun that follows the preposition. This means that the noun *midday* must be marked in the dictionary with some temporal feature (e.g. semtype=time), while nouns like *school* must be marked with some locational feature (e.g. semtype=location).

We are assuming that semantic relations attach to prepositions. More properly, a semantic relation describes the role which the whole prepositional phrase, not just the preposition, plays in relation to its head, but it is convenient to allow the preposition to carry this feature too, in order to formulate the above translation rules. A prepositional phrase marked with the semantic relation TIME, for example, might indicate the time at which the action indicated by the verb takes place, while a phrase marked with the semantic relation PLACE might indicate the location at which it took place.

Although these features would solve many problems in translating prepositions, the semantic relations expressed by PLACE and TIME are not always fine grained enough. We can, for example, distinguish two different types of usage for locational *at*: '(to be) at school' indicates a position, whereas '(to shoot) at the goal' indicates a movement towards a certain place. We could decompose the semantic relation into two separate relations, say PLACE_POSITION for the first phrase, and PLACE_PATH for the second phrase. Note that the calculation of these new semantic relations will depend not only on the semantic features of the nouns that follow them, but crucially on the type of verb.

Our brief example illustrates some of the problems we face when trying to assign semantic relations to prepositional phrases, or other categories. First, it is difficult to know what a canonical set of semantic relations might look like, since the refinement or granularity required (that is, the number of distinctions we want to make) depends to some extent on the type of translation problem encountered. Secondly, the finer the granularity, the more elaborate the feature system will have to be, in order to differentiate nouns, for example. Finally, the calculation of semantic relations depends on a number of factors, including as we have seen the type of verb and the type of the following noun.

We have described semantic features as more or less optional additions to representations — the addition of a semantic feature may serve to disambiguate a representation, by indicating which sense of a word is involved, but the representation is still conceived of as a structure consisting of lexical items (words). A more radical idea is to take the semantic features as exhausting the meaning of words, and to replace the lexical items by the appropriate set of features. Thus, one would have representations with (+HUMAN, +MASCULINE, +ADULT, ...) in place of the lexical item *man*. The idea is that the meanings of lexical items can be decomposed into sets of semantic primitives. Since such sets of semantic primitives might well be universal, one can in this way approach the goal of an interlingua. Here one cannot manage satisfactorily simply with sets of features, however. Instead, one needs to produce structures in which the predicates are semantic primitives. For example, the representation of *kill* might be along the following lines:

(4)   CAUSE [BECOME [NOT [ALIVE]]]

As we have already noted in Chapter 4 there are some doubts in general about the feasibility and advisability of this process of lexical decomposition. For example, there is a small but significant difference in meaning between *kill* and *cause to become not alive* — in particular, where a 'killing' is a single event, a 'causing to become not alive' involves at least two events (a 'causing', and a 'dying'), and if the causal chain that links a particular event to dying is long enough, one may admit that the event caused the dying, but not want to say there has been a 'killing'. Of course, these doubts depend on what one thinks the relation is between the semantic primitives like CAUSE, BECOME, etc., and English words like *cause*, *become*, etc., and also on the assumption that there is no semantic primitive KILL. Notice that, while a collection of semantic primitives that includes KILL is going to be quite large (perhaps in the order of a thousand primitives), this is still far less than the vocabulary one finds in normal use — so there may still be some value in semantic decomposition, even if the number of primitives that words decompose into is quite large.

So far we have concentrated our discussion of semantics on the meaning of words, but semantics is also concerned with linguistic 'systems' such as tense and aspect and determination, all of which are of considerable importance in translation. Consider the problem of how to translate the present tense in French into English, where there are at least three possibilities, exemplified in the following:

(5)   a.   Elle vit à Londres.

       b.   She lives in London.

(6)   a.   Elle vit à Londres depuis le mois dernier.

       b.   She has lived in London since last month.

(7)   a.   Elle mange son dîner.

       b.   She is eating her dinner.

Of course, one could try to formulate rules which describe the conditions under which French present tense is realized as English present, English present perfect, or present progressive, but such rules would be very complex. A more attractive possibility is to try to find some more abstract representation which directly describes the temporal and aspectual relations that these sentences involve. Here we will outline one type of approach.

The English tense system is used to convey two different types of information. One is the time of the event — both the present simple *I sing* and the present progressive *I am singing* describe an event in the present. The other is the nature of the event — e.g. the progressive stresses that the event is 'in progress'. Henceforth we shall reserve the word **tense** to mean the time of an event and use the word **aspect** to refer to the way the event is viewed (as an on-going or completed process, a state, or a simple event, etc.). We will use the term **time reference** to cover both tense and aspect.

We can think of tense as expressing a relation between the time of the event and the time of speech. Thus, with the present (*I sing*), the time of the event (which we could call E) overlaps with the time of speech (which we could call S). Contrast the future (*I shall sing*) where the time of the event follows the time of speech (E follows S), or the past, where E precedes S. However, this is not sufficient to distinguish all the different temporal forms of the English verb. There is a problem with the past, where our definition of tense does not allow us to differentiate between the simple past (*I sang*) and the pluperfect (or past-perfect — *I had sung*), since in both cases the time of the event is prior to the time of speech. One solution is to define an additional point of time, called the **reference time** (R). Consider, for example, the sentence:

(8)   At two o'clock Sam had already eaten.

At two o'clock specifies a moment in time which precedes the time of speech, but which is not the time of event. Two o'clock is not the time at which John ate, but the time by which he had already eaten. The temporal relations of this sentence can be expressed as follows, where < means 'precedes':

$$E < R, \; R < S$$

This indicates that the time of the event (E) precedes the reference time (R), and R precedes the time of speech (S).

We can now distinguish the pluperfect from the simple past by stipulating that in both cases the time of the event precedes the time of speech (E < S), but while in the pluperfect the time of the event precedes the reference time (E < R), in the simple past the time of event and the reference time coincide (E = R).

We can do something similar to distinguish the present perfect (9) from the other tenses. Here too the event described precedes the speech time, but there is a sense in which sentences in the present perfect are 'about' the present (for example, (9) would be appropriate only if Sam's previous eating habits are still of current relevance). We can capture this by making reference time and speech time coincide (R=S).

(9)   Sam has eaten snails.

This gives the following picture:

	Sam had eaten.	pluperfect	R<S,E<R
(10)	Sam ate.	simple past	R<S,E=R
	Sam has eaten.	present perfect	R=S,E<R

We now have the apparatus to represent the difference in tense and aspect between the examples above. Of course, having a way of representing tense and aspect values as above is one thing, calculating the representations for particular inputs is another. This is no trivial task, since the tense and aspect values of the verb will in general depend on many factors, including the form of the verb, and whether it is modified by any time adverbials such as *yesterday* and *tomorrow*.

However, let us assume that we have calculated the tense and aspect values of the following sentence, and see how this helps translation.

(11)   Elle vit à Londres depuis le mois dernier.

This sentence might receive a semantic representation along the lines of Figure 7.1. The feature `time-ref` encodes the information about tense and aspect, in particular, the fact that the reference time coincides with the time of speech, and the event time precedes the reference time (and hence also the time of speech).

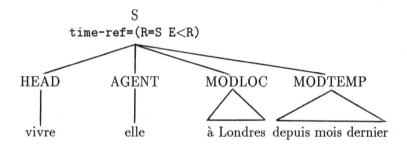

Figure 7.1 Representation Indicating Time Values after French Analysis

Since the information encoded by the `time-ref` feature is presumed to be preserved in translation, this feature can treated as an interlingual feature, and thus can be mapped unchanged onto the target language (in this case English), giving the representation in Figure 7.2.

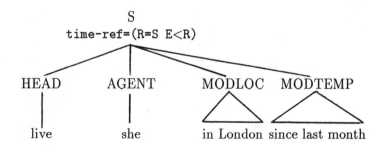

Figure 7.2 Representation after Transfer but before English Synthesis

The verb form *has lived* can then be generated from this representation by English synthesis, giving the translation (12). Other `time-ref` values would be realized differently — in principle, the correct translations of the examples above can be obtained.

(12)   She has lived in London since last month.

This treatment of tense and aspect involves a lot of complicated machinery, and is not entirely unproblematic. Nevertheless it gives some indication of how one might attempt to handle the difficult problem of tense and aspect in MT.

7.3   Pragmatics

Recall that we made a distinction between semantics, or context-independent meaning, and pragmatics, or context-dependent meaning. The term 'context' is used ambiguously, to refer to the rest of the text in which a sentence occurs (sometimes referred to as the discourse), and to circumstances external to the text itself, such as who the author of the text is, and the social setting in which it occurs, which also contribute to its interpretation.

To see why the discourse is important, let us consider the translation of **anaphoric pronouns**. Anaphoric pronouns are those which refer back to some **antecedent** earlier in the text, as the pronoun *it* in (13) refers back to its antecedent *the cake*.

(13)   Sam took the cake from the table. Then he ate it.

Take the translation of (13) from English into French. We know that *it* must refer back to some singular noun in the previous text or discourse. It has been shown that it is very often the case that the antecedent of a pronoun is in the same sentence or in the immediately preceding sentence. Assuming that these are the first sentences in our text, then *it* can potentially refer back to one of three NPs, namely *Sam*, *the cake* or *the table*. The syntactic facts of English constrain the pronoun to agree in number and gender with its antecedent, so *it* being a neuter pronoun cannot possibly refer to *Sam*, which is either masculine or feminine. That leaves us with the choice of either *cake* or *table*. One might wonder at this stage whether we need to decide between the two at all, or whether we can preserve the ambiguity of *it* in translation. It turns out that French, like English, requires a pronoun to agree in number and gender with its antecedent. However, since *cake* translates as the masculine noun *gâteau* in French and *table* as the feminine noun *table*, this means that we do have to decide which noun the pronoun *it* refers back to, in order to translate *it* either as *le* (where it would be interpreted as referring to *le gâteau* — cake) or as *la* (where it would refer back to *la table* in the translation of the first sentence). In the above example we can use selectional restrictions on the type of object that *eat* can have (namely 'edible' objects) to exclude, or at least 'disprefer', *table* as an antecedent for *it*. This leaves *cake* as the best candidate. Providing rules which allow this sort of process to be performed automatically is not too difficult, but unfortunately resolving pronoun reference is not generally that simple.

First of all, let us consider cases where the pronoun antecedent is not in the current or preceding sentence. An example might be the following dialogue between two speakers A and B, which appeared in Chapter 6.

(14) a. A: Now insert the cartridge at the back.
     b. B: Okay.
     c. A: By the way, did you order more toner today?
     d. B: Yes, I got some when I picked up the new paper.
     e. A: OK, how far have you got?
     f. Did you get $\boxed{\text{it}}$ fixed?

It in the last sentence of (14) refers to the cartridge, although the cartridge was last mentioned in the first sentence. Looking for the pronoun's antecedent in the present or preceding sentence this time will not get us the right result. To find the antecedent, we need to think of the previous discourse not as an unstructured whole, or a simple sequence of sentences, but rather as a series of 'segments', where a segment is a stretch of discourse in which the (not necessarily adjacent) sentences address the same topic. Cue phrases such as *by the way*, and *next* provide clues to where one segment ends and another one begins. We then constrain the referent of an anaphor to belong to the same discourse segment as the anaphor.

In the example (14), there are three obvious referents for *it*: the cartridge (14a), toner (14c), and paper (14d). However, sentences (14c) and (14d) which form a digression, that is, a discourse segment with a topic (namely toner) distinct from the main discourse (and whose purpose is not directly related to the purpose of the main discourse — in this case the purpose of reassembling the printer). The start of the new segment is signalled by *by the way* and the resumption of the old segment is signalled by *OK*. It is for this reason that the expressions *toner* and *new paper* cannot provide referents for *it*. In fact, once discourse structure is taken into account, it can be seen that *the cartridge* is the only possible antecedent, because it is the only possible antecedent which is in the same discourse segment as the anaphor.[1]

Faced with two competing candidates for pronominal reference in a segment, there is another fact about discourse that we can exploit to get at their resolution, and

---

[1] This is a simplification, of course. For one thing, *it* could be used to refer to something outside the discourse, to some entity which is not mentioned, but pointed at, for example. For another thing, there are some other potential antencedents, such as *the back* in (14a), and it could be that Speaker A is returning to the digression in sentence (14f). Though the discourse structure can helps to resolve pronoun-antecedent relations, discovering the discourse structure poses serious problems.

```
┌─────────────────────────Top Level Discourse Segment ──────┐
│ A: Now insert the cartridge at the back.                   │
│                                                            │
│ B: Okay.                                                   │
│   ┌───────────────────Embedded Discourse Segment ──────┐  │
│   │ A: By the way, did you order some more toner?       │  │
│   │                                                     │  │
│   │ B: Yes, I got some when I picked up the new paper.  │  │
│   └─────────────────────────────────────────────────────┘ │
│                                                            │
│ A: Okay, how far have you got?                             │
│                                                            │
│    Did you get it fixed?                                   │
└────────────────────────────────────────────────────────────┘
```

Figure 7.3 Discourse Structure

this is the notion of **focus**. At any time in a discourse segment there is an object which is the prime candidate for pronominal reference, and this element is called the focus. Different suggestions have been made as to how to identify the focus. Often, there are syntactic signals. For example, in the following example, the focus is much more likely to be *Kim*, than *Sam*, and *Kim* is more likely to be the antecedent of a pronoun in the following sentence.

(15)   It was Kim who Sam telephoned. $\boxed{\text{She}}$ was in the bath.

The focus of a sentence is also often the NP that has the THEME role in the previous sentence (the THEME role includes what we have been calling the PATIENT role, but is slightly more general). This is the case with *Kim* in (15), which reinforces the structural cue. But even in the following sequence, where there are no clear structural clues, *key* is the THEME and hence most likely to be the focus of the first sentence (and therefore *key* is preferred to *doormat* as the referent of *it* in the second sentence).

(16)   She put the key under the doormat.
         When she came home, she found that $\boxed{\text{it}}$ had been stolen.

Thus, information about discourse structure is of some help in the resolution of pronoun-antecedent relations. However, employing knowledge of discourse alone will not enable us to resolve the reference of all pronouns, as we shall see below.

Let us first look briefly at the other side of pragmatics we mentioned, the context of use. It is obvious that the identity of the speaker/writer and the addressee will affect the translation of indexical expressions such as *I* and *you* since some languages make a distinction, for instance between *you* (singular) and *you* (plural). Similarly, in languages where an adjective agrees in gender with its noun (as in French, for example), it will be necessary to know not only the number of the speakers and the addressees, but also their gender in translating an example like *Are you happy?*. In addition, knowing the relationship between the addresser and addressee can be important for translation. The degree of formality between them will affect, for example, the choice of either *vous* (formal) or *tu* (informal) as the translation of *you* when translating from English into French. In many languages, including Japanese, the social relation of speaker and hearer can determine the form of verb, and even the choice of verb. There are, for example, different verbs for giving as from a superior to an inferior, and for giving as an inferior to a superior.[2]

We have said that a sentence has to be interpreted relative to both the previous discourse and to the situation in which it is uttered. In addition, it seems that the meaning of a message is shaped by its producer's intentions and beliefs. For example, how we interpret (17) depends on whether the speaker intended it as a command (to close the front cover), or as an statement (describing the state the cover is likely to be in).

(17)   The front cover should be closed.

Of course, the interpretation also depends on the hearer inferring correctly what the speaker's intentions are. Whether the above sentence is interpreted as a command or statement will affect its translation in some languages.

7.4   Real World Knowledge

The above discussion may lead one to suspect that all the knowledge we need to extract the meaning from texts and translate them can be got from the texts or their contexts. This is, however, clearly not the case, as the following classic examples show:

(18) a.   Little Johnny was very upset. He had lost his toy train. Then he found it. It was in his pen .

      b.   I saw the soldiers aim at the women, and I saw several of them fall.

      c.   The council refused the women a permit because they advocated violence.

      d.   Sue went to put the key under the doormat. When she lifted it up, a cockroach quickly scampered across the path.

---

[2]Politeness dictates that giving by the hearer to the speaker is normally giving 'downwards' (*kureru*), so this is the verb used to describe requests, and giving by the speaker to the hearer is normally giving 'upwards' (*ageru*), so this is the verb used to describe offers, etc.

In the first example, the problem is the interpretation of *pen* — it must be playpen, not writing pen, because (roughly) for A to be *in* B, A must be smaller than B, and toy trains are smaller than playpens, but not writing pens. In the second example, the question is who fell over — soldiers or women? In general, we reason that 'aiming at' is often followed by firing at, and that firing at is usually followed by those aimed at falling over, and only rarely followed by those who do the aiming falling over. In the third case, most people understand that it is the women who advocate violence — this seems a normal enough ground for refusing a permit (of course, it could be that the council advocated violence, and refused the women a permit so as to enrage them, and incite them to violence). In the case of (18d), we exploit the fact that cockroaches are more likely to hide under doormats than under keys to work out the most likely interpretation of *it*.

In order to translate these examples one will often have to decide what the pronounsrefer to, because many languages use different forms, depending on properties of the antecedent. For example, translating (18d) into German involves deciding what *it* refers to, since the possible candidates are the key or the doormat, which have different genders in German, which the pronoun reflects. Similar issues are involved in translating (18b,c). The knowledge that is deployed here appears to be non-linguistic knowledge, and the reasoning is more or less 'common sense', perhaps with some small amount of specialist knowledge of the subject matter. This is perhaps less obvious in the first case, where one may think that the meaning of *in* is central, but it is surely clear for the others — it is nothing to do with the *meaning* of *aim at* that it is often followed by those aimed at falling over. However, even in the playpen – writing pen case, we can surely imagine a bizarre situation where little Johnny's playpen is in fact tiny, and he has just been given a large fountain pen as a present. In such a situation, the interpretation would be changed, but not because the meaning of the words had changed.

The real world knowledge that is involved here includes common sense reasoning, as well as general knowledge, and facts about certain more specialized domains. Representing and manipulating such knowledge automatically is one of the outstanding research questions of our time, and the raison d' être of an entire discipline (Artificial Intelligence, AI). The problems of representing and manipulating linguistic knowledge pale into insignificance compared to the problems posed by real world knowledge.

One of the problems it raises is that (unlike most linguistic knowledge, in particular, most knowledge of syntax and semantics) such knowledge is generally 'defeasible', that is, subject to revision, and not guaranteed correct[3] – humans have little trouble assuming one thing most of the time, but managing with a contradictory assumption on occasions (as in the small playpen example above). This is extremely difficult

---

[3] As noted above, knowledge about selectional restrictions is unusual in being defeasible in just this way: the restriction that the AGENT of *eat* is ANIMATE is only a preference, or default, and can be overridden. This leads some to think that it is not strictly speaking linguistic knowledge at all. In general, the distinction between linguistic and real world knowledge is not always very clear.

to automate. A second problem is the huge amount of such knowledge we seem to have (knowledge about the relative sizes of almost everything, for example). However, there are some methods of representation that are useful for some kinds of knowledge.

One particularly useful representation is the so called **Semantic Net** which can be used for representing 'is a' relations (such as 'a dog is a mammal'). Figure 7.4 gives a small part of such a network.

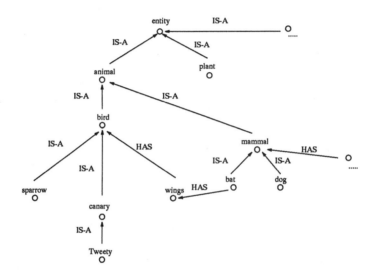

Figure 7.4 A Fragment of a Semantic Net

Intuitively, the nodes in such a network stand for things, and the links between them are relations. This means that it can easily be generalized for other sorts of relations. For example, adding other objects, and using a 'part of' relation, one could represent the fact that (say) a printer is made up of various components, and the fact that these are in turn made up of subcomponents, etc. Such information might be important in understanding sentences like the following:

(19) Put the toner in the cartridge in the reservoir.

Knowing that the reservoir does not have a cartridge as a part would allow one to work out that this is an instruction to put the toner *which is* in the cartridge in the reservoir, rather than an instruction to put the toner in a particular cartridge (i.e. the one that is in the reservoir).

An alternative approach to general knowledge representation is to attempt to formulate it as collections of 'facts' and 'rules'. Examples of facts might be the following, which indicate individuals' departments:

```
dept(jones,sales).

dept(brown,sales).

dept(smith,personnel).

...
```

The following rule might be used to indicate that two individuals are colleagues, if they work for the same department ('A and B are colleagues if A works in department D, and B works in department D'):

```
colleagues(A,B) <- dept(A,D), dept(B,D).
```

One problem with both the semantic net, and the 'facts and rules' representations are that they are both rather 'small', or loosely organized collections of knowledge. This is not how at least some kinds of human knowledge seem to be. For example, what the reader knows about her own home is probably not spread around as sets of unconnected facts. In some way, it seems to be organized into a coherent, structured whole. (One way of seeing this is by describing your home to someone – what you will probably do is take them on a sort of mental tour, which closely mirrors the physical organization of your home). Similarly, for many practical purposes, such as eating in restaurants, one does not seem to have a collection of facts and rules, but a structured 'script' of things that typically happen. A great deal of effort has been devoted to the issue of just what the right kinds of structure are for knowledge representation. The generic name for such larger knowledge structures is *frames*. We will give an example of such a representation in Chapter 10, but we will not pursue the idea here, because to a great extent these larger knowledge structures can be built out of smaller ones, such as the ones we have described.

We now have a way of representing at least some real world knowledge. The question is, how can it be manipulated? This is a complex and not particularly well-understood matter, and we will give only the barest outline. However, two points should be emphasised: (a) that as a whole, the general problem of manipulating knowledge of the world in anything like the way humans do is unsolved, and may even prove to be insoluble (this is something of a philosophical question); but (b) under some restricted circumstances, something useful can be done. The kind of restricted circumstances we have in mind are where there are relatively few things to think about, and the ways they are related and can be organized and interact are very limited. An example of this sort might be the internal workings of a printer – it is possible to list all the 'things' (the printer parts), their relations, and relevant properties (cf. again Chapter 10).

One thing that manipulating this knowledge means is using it to answer questions, and draw inferences. For example, given that one knows that Smith works in the Finance Department, and Jones works in the Finance Department, how can one work out that Smith and Jones are colleagues? Given that Tweety is a bird, and that birds have wings, how can one work out that Tweety has wings? Of course, given the representations above, these questions are not so hard to answer. In the first case we have provided a rule, the only problem is to find the rule, and follow it. In the other case, we have exemplified a datastructure (a semantic net), the only problem is to define a procedure that allows one to use it.

In the first case, one could proceed as follows. In order to answer the question of whether Brown and Jones are colleagues, one should look for appropriate facts and rules. Assuming there are no appropriate facts, we have only the rule given above. This tells us that A and B are colleagues if A works in department D, and B works in department D. We can treat these two conditions as fresh questions, and answer them in the same way, except that now we have relevant facts, which will tell us that Brown works in sales, and Jones works in sales. We have now answered all the subsidiary questions in the affirmative. It follows that we have also answered the initial question.

In the case of the semantic nets, we might define a procedure that answers questions in the following way: to answer the question of whether an object has a property, first look to see if the property is linked to the object by a HAS link. If it does, answer 'yes'. If it does not, inspect each of the IS-A links that end at the object, asking the same question at each one. Thus, though it is not indicated that Tweety HAS wings, because Tweety IS-A bird, and bird HAS wings, we can infer that Tweety HAS wings, and answer questions about whether Tweety has wings.

This is a somewhat vague description. However, one may be able to see that some things are possible, but also that this approach to representing and manipulating real world knowledge is insufficient. These are some of the things that are lacking.

1 We have not provided a way of handling defeasible rules, or dealing with vague or 'fuzzy' predicates such as *tall*, *hot*, etc. For example, penguins are birds, but cannot fly. Working on the principles just described, one would expect a system to assume that they could fly. The rules we have given are interpreted as general or universal — in fact, they should only be interpreted as indicating defaults. Though there are some partial techniques for dealing with this, how best to automate default reasoning remains an open research question. Similarly, the categories we have mentioned in the discussion are generally rather clear, in the sense that whether something is a bird, or a mammal seems to be a question that can have a clear, yes or no answer. This is not the case with vague predicates like *hot*, or *tall*. In these cases, not only is there usually some idea of a standard of comparison ("Hot compared to what?"), which must be inferred from the context, in some way, but the question of whether something is hot is one that often lacks a clear answer

— rather than yes, or no, one may be inclined to answer a question like *Is it hot?*, with a reply like 'a little', or 'somewhat'. Again, though there are some interesting theories, it is mainly an open research question how to model the sort of reasoning with fuzzy categories that humans can perform.

2 We have suggested how one can answer questions, once they are posed — but not how one can reason 'forwards' independent of particular questions. For example, if someone says *The printer is broken*, hearers may typically draw a whole range of conclusions (such as "I will not be able to print the next chapter", or "We will have to call an engineer"), without particular questions being posed. The problem here is that while the range of inferences drawn is large, it is not as large as it could be (it could be infinite, since every conclusion will typically lead to new chains of inferences being started), and it is not clear how to control this process.

3 We have not given any indication of how one would solve the actual problems raised by the examples in (18). One could, of course, simply record information about the relative sizes of known objects as facts, and in the same way associate with other classes of objects default sizes (e.g. sparrows are typically less than 10cms tall), but this does not look very plausible as a model of how humans represent this knowledge.

4 We have not said anything about how one might reasonably set about encoding all the knowledge that seems to be needed, even assuming that one had the 'right' format. The problem is that we cannot anticipate just what particular pieces of real world knowledge a system may need in general. The amount of knowledge that human writers assume, and readers supply without apparent effort or reflection is simply vast, and highly unpredictable, and the effort involved in actually encoding it in this sort of way is prohibitive. Far more feasible is the aim of equipping a computer with facts about a specific domain. As we will describe in Chapter 10, some advanced so-called Knowledge-Based systems are attempting to do just that.

7.5   Summary

In this chapter we have looked at three kinds of knowledge that seem to be involved in solving some sorts of translation problems, namely: semantic, pragmatic, and real world knowledge. Particular problems we have looked at include the translation of prepositions, of tense and aspect, and of pronouns. As we stated at the beginning of the chapter, the point to stress as regards such knowledge is that its representation and manipulation pose many unsolved problems, and one should not expect to find techniques which exploit it in existing commercial MT systems (it follows that, for the most part, existing commercial MT systems may be expected to lack adequate or general treatments of the sorts of problem which require such knowledge). On the other hand, such processing is not *totally* beyond the reach of current theory. In particular, within certain limits, and in restricted domains, techniques of semantic, pragmatic, and 'real world' knowledge processing can be exploited with some success.

7.6 Further Reading

Introductions to linguistic semantics include [Hurford and Heasley, 1983; Kempson, 1977], and, at a rather more advanced level [Cann, 1993; Chierchia and McConnell-Ginet, 1990].

The discussion of tense and aspect given here is inspired by that used in the EUROTRA project, which is described in [Allegranza et al., 1991; Van Eynde, 1993a]. This, in its turn, is inspired by the work of [Bruce, 1972], and ultimately [Reichenbach, 1947].

As regards pragmatics, [Levinson, 1983; Leech, 1983] are useful introductions. Relevant work on discourse structure includes [Grosz and Sidner, 1986; Pustejovsky, 1987]. The treatment of common sense inference and real world knowledge is the field of Artificial Intelligence, see for example [Rich, 1983; Tennant, 1981; Barr and Fiegenbaum, 1981; Shapiro, 1987]. On semantic nets, see [Sowa, 1984]. The perspective we have taken in this Chapter is rather that suggested by the programming language Prolog. For an easy introduction to this see [Rogers, 1986]. For more advanced material directed at AI applications, see [Bratko, 1986], for material focussed on NLP applications, see [Gazdar and Mellish, 1989].

The *play-pen – writing-pen* example is from Bar-Hillel [Bar-Hillel, 1951].

Chapter 8

Input

8.1 Introduction

In the scenario we imagined in Chapter 2, the text was delivered in the form of a machine-readable document, having been prepared in such a way as to facilitate translation. This is an important time saver. In this chapter, we describe how the full potential of machine readable texts can be exploited in three ways: first, by adopting the notion of an 'electronic document' and embedding an MT system in a complete document processing system; second, by restricting the form of input by using simplified or **controlled language**; and third, by restricting both the form, and the subject matter of the input texts to those that fall within a **sublanguage** — it is here that the immediate prospects for MT are greatest. The common theme of this chapter is how the successful application of MT can be enhanced by ensuring that the input to the system is 'appropriate'. Briefly, the message is this: having texts in machine readable form is a prerequisite for sensible use of MT, but one can get much better results by (i) adopting certain standard formats for the input, (ii) controlling the input, so that problematic constructions, etc., are avoided, and (iii) where possible, tailoring the MT systems to the language of particular domains.

8.2 The Electronic Document

8.2.1 Basic Ideas

Every text that is not delivered as an electronic document on a floppy disc, a magnetic tape, or via a computer network will have to be put into the system manually. Re-typing a text into the computer solely to make it available for MT is unlikely to be cost-effective — it would often be quicker to have the text translated directly by a human translator. In recent years it has become practicable to use an optical character reader (OCR) to input text available only in printed form. Clearly this is much quicker than re-typing, but checking for and correcting scanning errors can be time-consuming.

However, if as is the case with ETRANS as described in Chapter 2, the MT system fits into an overall document production system (DPS), then text can be created, translated, re-edited and generally prepared for publication within the same electronic environment. In the first part of this chapter we will explore this notion of an electronic document in some detail.

The Risks of Office Automation

Electronic text is simply text which is available in a machine readable form. For example, electronic text is produced by ordinary office word processors. At its simplest, such a text is just a sequence of characters, and, for the characters in use in general computing (i.e. the English alphabet, normal punctuation characters, plus characters such as the 'space' character, the 'line-feed' character, etc.) there is a standard representation provided by the ASCII[1] codes, which associates each character with a seven or eight bit code (i.e. a number — e.g. a is ASCII 97, b is ASCII 98, A is ASCII 65, the 'space' character is ASCII 32). Unfortunately,

---

[1] ASCII stands for American Standard Code for Information Interchange.

this standard is not sufficient for encoding the letters of foreign alphabets and their accents, even those based on the Roman alphabet, let alone non-Roman alphabets, and characters in non-alphabetic scripts, such as Japanese characters (Kanji). One approach to such alphabets is to extend the ASCII codes beyond those needed by English. Another is to represent foreign accents and special characters by sequences of standard ASCII characters. For example, a German *u* with umlaut (*ü*) might be represented thus: \"{u}.

One problem is that there is (as yet) no genuine accepted standard beyond basic ASCII, with the further complication that many word processors use non-ASCII representations 'internally', as a way of representing text format (e.g. information about typeface, underlining, etc.) This lack of standards means that it is necessary to use special conversion programs if one wants to freely import and export text from different languages and a variety of DPSs (such as word processors). Even when such programs exist, they do not always preserve all the information (e.g. some information about format may be lost).

Part of a general solution to these problems, however, is to distinguish two components of a printed document: the text itself (a sequence of words and characters); and its rendition — the form in which it appears on the page (or screen). For example, consider a title or heading. There are the words which make up the title — perhaps a noun phrase such as 'The Electronic Document' — and the particular presentation or rendition of those words on the page. In this book all section and chapter headings are aligned with the left margin and different levels of heading (chapter, section, subsection) are printed in a distinctive typeface and separated by a standard space from the preceding and following paragraphs of text.

If we think about this distinction between text and rendition in electronic terms, it is easy to see that we have to code both the characters in the text, and indicate how we intend parts of that text to appear on screen or in printed form. In the early days of electronic text handling, this problem was solved in a rather direct and obvious fashion: the author would type in not only the substance of the text but also some special codes at appropriate places to tell the printer to switch into the appropriate type faces and point size. For example, in typing in a title the author would carefully insert an appropriate number of carriage returns (non-printing characters which start a newline) to get a nice spacing before and after. She would also make sure the title was centred or left-aligned as required, and finally she would type in special codes (say \[223\[-447) before and after the title string to switch the printer into a bold typeface with 24 'points' to the inch and back to its usual font and size immediately afterwards.

There are three evident problems with such a procedure:

1 The codes used are likely to be specific to particular printers or word processing set-ups and hence the electronic document will not be directly portable to other systems for revision, integration with other documents or printing.

2 The author is required to spend some of her time dealing with rendition problems — a task that (prior to the advent of electronic systems) had always been conveniently delegated to the compositor in a printing house.

3 If at some point it is decided that a different rendition of headings is required, someone has to go through the entire document and replace all the codes and characters associated with the rendition of each heading.

The printer codes are a sort of tiny little program for a particular printer. The next development was to replace these rather specific programs by some means of stating directly "I want this in 24 point Roman boldface" — perhaps by a 'markup' like this: '`\roman\24pt\bf` '. Each printer or word processor can then be equipped with a special program (a so-called 'driver') which interprets this high-level code and sends the printer or screen appropriate specific low-level codes. Providing everyone used exactly the same high-level codes in all systems, the problem of portability would be solved.

However, there is another way of tackling the rendition problem. When one thinks about it abstractly, the only thing that the author really needs to put into the text is some markup which says (in effect) 'This is a heading', or 'This is a footnote' or 'This is an item in an item list' and so on. Each piece of text is thus identified as being an instance of some class of text elements. With such markup, the author no longer has to worry about *how* each such marked document element is going to be printed or shown on screen — that task can be delegated to the document designer (the modern equivalent of a compositor). The document designer can specify an association between each type of document element and the high-level rendition codes she wants it to have. In other words, she can say that she wants all headings to be printed in 24 point boldface Roman. The document handling system then ensures that headings etc. are displayed and printed as required.

This type of markup, where the author simply identifies particular pieces of text as being instances of particular document elements, is known as descriptive or 'intensional' ('intentional') markup. This notion is fundamental to all modern document processing systems and techniques. Not only does this provide flexibility in how text is rendered, provided that the way in which markup is made is consistent from system to system, the result is that electronic documents can be freely passed between systems.

We can now be a little more precise about the notion of an electronic document: it contains electronic or machine-readable text with descriptive markup codes which may be used to determine the rendition and other usages of the document. Before we go on to give an idea of how this can be exploited for MT, it may be worth a brief description of the standard descriptive markup: SGML (Standardised General Markup Language) which is specified by the International Standards Organization. It is our belief that in the next few years no serious commercial MT system will be supplied without some means of handling SGML.

SGML specifies that, ordinarily, text will be marked up in the way shown in the last example above, i.e. with document elements surrounded by their names in angle brackets. An office memo marked up in SGML might look like the example below. In addition to the actual text, various pairs of SGML tags delimiting the memo elements can be seen here. The memo as a whole starts with **<Memo>** and ends with **</Memo>** (where / indicates the closing delimiter). In between the Memo tag pair we find the sub-elements of the memo, also marked-up with paired tags (**<To>**... **</To>**, **<From>** .. **</From>**, **<Body>**... **<P>**..**</P>**...**</Body>**).

A Memo Marked Up in SGML

```
<Memo>
<To>Mary Dale, Purchasing</To>
<From>Tony Burrows</From>
<Body>
<P>We would like to order 4 Sun ELCs with an
additional 8M of memory.  We don't need any external
drives.</P>
<P>By the way, have you managed to get any more info
on SGML parsers for PCs?  Or on SGML parsers for
anything?</P>
</Body>
</Memo>
```

The relationship between SGML tags, and the way text is actually rendered is given by an association table, such a table might say, e.g. that the body of a memo should be separated from the previous part by a horizontal line. When actually printed, this memo might look as in Figure 8.1:

The tagging principles of SGML are intended to extend to very complex and highly structured documents. Imposing such a structure not only allows very fine, and flexible control of how documents are printed, it can also allow easy access to and manipulation of information in documents, and straightforward consistency checking[2].

One thing the SGML standard does not do is try to specify a standard inventory of all possible document elements. Users are perfectly free to define their own document types and to specify the elements in those documents. SGML provides

---

[2] For example, suppose one has a printer manual marked up in this way, with special markup used for the names of printer components wherever they occur. It would be very easy to extract a list of printer parts automatically, together with surrounding text. This text might be a useful addition to a parts database. As regards consistency, it would be easy to check that each section conforms to a required pattern — e.g. that it contains a list of all parts mentioned in the section.

MEMORANDUM

To: Mary Dale, Purchasing
From: Tony Burrows

We would like to order 4 Sun ELCs with an additional
8M of memory. We don't need any external drives.

By the way, have you managed to get any more info
on SGML parsers for PCs? Or on SGML parsers for
anything?

Figure 8.1   How a Memo Marked Up in SGML Might Appear When Printed

a special method of doing this known as a **Document Type Definition** (DTD).
A DTD is a sort of formal grammar specifying all such relations in a particular
type of document. For example, such a grammar might say that all Memos (all
our Memos at least) contain a *To* element followed by a *From* element followed by
a *Body* element, which itself contains at least one *Paragraph* followed by zero or
more *Paragraphs*. This means that a *Memo* has the following sort of DTD (grossly
simplified):

```
Memo → To, From, Body

Body → Paragraph, Paragraph*
```

Using a DTD has several advantages:

1 The DTD makes sure that documents are truly portable between different
   SGML document systems; the document system reads the accompanying DTD
   to find out what sort of elements will be in the document and how they will be
   arranged with respect to each other. Thus, the document processing system
   knows what to expect when it encounters a document which is an instance of
   a certain DTD.

2 It ensures that documents of a particular type (e.g. user manuals) are always
   structurally consistent with each other. It suffices to define a DTD for the
   class of user manuals and then the SGML document processing system will
   ensure that all documents produced by that DTD will indeed have the same
   overall structure. In short, DTDs help to promote a certain rigour which is
   extremely desirable in technical documentation.

3 The use of DTDs in document preparation allows authors to deal directly with the content of texts whilst having little or no direct contact with the actual markup used. What happens with the usual sort of SGML system is that there is a window offering the author a choice of document entities appropriate for the document she is preparing or revising. This list of document entities is obtained by reading the DTD for the document. For example, in a memo, there will be a choice of *To*, *From*, and *Body*. The author clicks on the appropriate element and the markup is entered into the text (perhaps invisibly). When actually typing in the *Body*, the choice is narrowed down to *Paragraph*. Whilst this is not particularly interesting for simple documents like memos, it is clear that it would be be immensely useful in constructing complex documents, and in document retrieval.

With this general idea of Electronic Documents and markup, we can look at how an MT system can exploit the fact that texts are represented in this way.

8.2.2 SGML Markup and MT Input

An MT system should only attempt to translate things that are translatable. Suppose that some text contains the acronym 'MAT', which refers to a company called 'Machine Aided Translation Ltd'. Clearly the correct translation of this is either just MAT again or some new acronym that reflects the translation of the underlying name — perhaps TAO in French, being the acronym for *Traduction Assistée par Ordinateur*, which itself is the translation of *Machine Aided Translation*. What is unquestionably incorrect is a translation of the form *pallaison*, this being the sort of mat that a cat might sit on. The reader may think that the MT system ought to have spotted that MAT cannot be a standard concrete noun because it is capitalised; but many MT systems routinely ignore capitals because they need to recognise ordinary words which can appear with an initial capital letter at the start of a sentence.

The way to deal with this sort of problem is to ensure that acronyms are recognised as a particular class of text elements and marked up as such. This might be done (a) either by the author when the text is being created or (b) by special tools used before translation which help translators to find acronyms and the like and mark them up accordingly. For example, a specialised search and replace tool inside the document pre-editor could look for all sequences of capitalised words and, after querying the translator to check whether a particular candidate sequence really is an acronym, insert the appropriate markers in the text. The point is that once the text is marked up, the MT system is in a much better situation to know that it is dealing with an untranslatable acronym and to treat it accordingly.

Similarly, consider figures and diagrams in a document. These consist usually of pictorial material, which is untranslatable, and a translatable text caption which characterises the pictorial material. Recognising the markup tags which indicate that the following material in the document is pictorial, the MT system can simply ignore everything until it encounters another tag telling it that it is about to see the caption, which it can translate as a normal piece of text. Equally, it is easy to ask the MT system to translate (say) just a single chapter, because the markup in the document will clearly identify the piece of text that constitutes the chapter. Markup is thus a powerful tool in controlling the MT process.

DTDs are particularly useful in MT. Some MT systems keep a copy of each sentence they have already encountered together with its translation (the post-edited version, if available). This habit is known in the industry as **Translation Memory**. Over the years, MT vendors have found that in some organizations much of the translation workload consists of entirely re-translating revised editions of technical manuals. These revised editions may contain as much as 90% of the material that was already present in the previous edition — and which was already translated and post-edited. Hence automatically recognising sentences already translated and retrieving the post-edited translation - as the Translation Memory technique allows — results in a 90% reduction in post-editing costs (and an enormous increase in the overall speed of the translation process). This is clearly very significant.

However, these sort of performance improvements are really the result of a defective documentation process. The problem is that the organization paying to have the translation done is not keeping proper track of which parts of a revised document really are different from the original version. Clearly only new or altered material really needs to be even considered for translation.

Within the SGML standard it is possible to add features to text elements to record when they were last altered, by whom and so on. This version control information can be maintained by the document system and it allows the user to extract revised elements. Indeed, the principle can be extended so that earlier versions of a given revised element are also kept, allowing the user to reconstruct any previous version of a document at any point.

The result of exercising proper version control in documentation is that only new elements for which there are no existing translations will be submitted to the translation process. In this way, the document processing system takes some of the burden otherwise carried by the MT system (viz, the 'Translation Memory' facility).

Another advantage of using DTDs in MT involves generalizing the notion of a document slightly, to introduce the notion of a 'multilingual document'. In SGML, this is largely a matter of altering the DTDs of monolingual document types. Take the Memo example: we can get a multilingual version by specifying that there is a copy of each document element for each language. Here is a revised (and still simplified) Memo DTD for two languages:

```
Memo → To, From, Body
```

```
Body  →  Paragraph, Paragraph*

Paragraph  →  Paragraph-L1, Paragraph-L2
```

There are now two types of Paragraph — Paragraphs in language one and Paragraphs in language 2. Each Paragraph element will contain one language 1 paragraph followed by one language 2 paragraph. (There are no language specific **To** and **From** elements because it is assumed that they contain only proper names). This sort of technique can be generalised to allow a document to carry text in arbitrarily many languages. Though this allows a document to contain text for more than one language, it does not require it — document elements can be empty — this would be the case for target language elements where the source element has not yet been translated.[3]

The important thing to understand here is that just because the simple multilingual DTD we have described 'interleaves' the elements for different languages (we have a paragraph for L1 followed by the corresponding paragraph for L2, etc.), this does not mean that we have to view the document that way. For example, a Memo in English, French and German can be viewed on the screen of a document processing system with all the English paragraphs, printed together, and the French paragraphs printed alongside, with the German paragraphs not shown at all. Part of the flexibility in the rendition of a marked-up document is that the text content of classes of elements can be hidden or shown at will. In practical terms, this means that a translator editing a multilingual document will have considerable flexibility in choosing the way in which that document is presented (on screen or on paper) and in choosing the type of element she wishes to see.

Turning back to the MT case, recall that in the scenario in Chapter 2, ETRANS takes the German text and then makes available the English translation in the multilingual document. It should now be much clearer how this works. Translatable elements from the source text are passed to the ETRANS system which then translates them. The translated text is then placed under the corresponding target language text elements (which, up that point, have been entirely empty of text). So far as is linguistically possible, the structure of the document is preserved.

In summary, it should be clear that the general idea of the Electronic Document is important within the context of MT and can make a considerable contribution to the successful integration of MT within the office environment.

---

[3] Although most elements of the structure are exactly matched, there may sometimes be differences. For example, if the document element Paragraph is composed of document element Sentence(s), it is perhaps unwise to insist that each Sentence in each language is paired exactly with a single corresponding Sentence in every other language, since frequently there is a tendency to distribute information across sentences slightly differently in different languages. However, at least for technical purposes, it is usually perfectly safe to assume that the languages are paired Paragraph by Paragraph, even though these units may contain slightly different numbers of sentences for each language.

8.3   Controlled Languages

The notion of controlled languages was introduced in Chapter 2 where we described it as a form of language usage restricted by grammar and vocabulary rules. The original idea arose during the 1930s, when a number of influential linguists and scholars devoted considerable effort to establishing a 'minimal' variety of English, a variety specifically designed to make English accessible to and usable by the largest possible number of people world wide. *Basic English*, as it was called, differed from previous attempts to construct universal languages in that it was a perfectly well-formed part of English, rather than some entirely artificial or hybrid construction such as Esperanto. One of the central ideas of the Basic English movement was that the number of general-purpose words needed for writing anything from a simple letter of receipt through to a major speech on the world economic situation could be a few hundred rather than the 75 000 upward available to skilled native speakers. This lexical economy was to be achieved in part by using 'operator verbs' with the set of nouns and adjectives to stand in for the vast number of derived verbs which are frequently used. For example, whereas in ordinary English we might write *The disc controller design was perfected over numerous revisions*, Basic English would say ... *was made perfect ...*, where *make* is one of the operator verbs and *perfect* one of the licensed Basic English adjectives.

The authors of Basic English explicitly recognised that the dictionary would need to be extended with special terminology for scientific and technical writing. However, even if a text contained terminology specific to a certain subject field, the general language component of the text could perfectly well be accommodated within Basic English. The important point remains that, for writing in a particular subject field, no more is needed than the Basic English dictionary together with a (relatively small) technical vocabulary for that field.

The idea was later taken on by English-language based (predominantly North American) corporations marketing capital goods on a world-wide basis. Rather than try to translate engine manuals and the like into every possible language that might be required, it was assumed that if they were written with sufficient care and attention, they could be read fairly easy by service engineers and mechanics with limited English skills.

Although controlled languages were introduced partly to avoid or reduce human translation costs, two important additional benefits were discovered. First, the readability and clarity of a controlled language technical text often seems better than uncontrolled texts — even for native English readers. Second, controlled languages produce better results with MT than uncontrolled languages.

The reasons for controlled languages' superior MT performance are easy to understand. First, the restricted vocabulary means that fewer words need to be added to the MT system dictionaries and more effort can be put into getting the entries which are required right. Second, the grammar component of the system can be tailored to handle all and only those constructions which are licensed by the controlled language specification, a specification which excludes the most difficult and ambiguous constructions anyway.

The PACE Writing Rules

- **Keep it short and simple:**

    1 Keep sentences short.

    2 Omit redundant words.

    3 Order the parts of the sentence logically.

    4 Don't change constructions in mid-sentence.

    5 Take care with the logic of *and* and *or*.

- **Make it explicit:**

    6 Avoid elliptical constructions.

    7 Don't omit conjunctions or relatives.

    8 Adhere to the PACE dictionary.

    9 Avoid strings of nouns.

    10 Do not use *-ing* unless the word appears thus in the PACE dictionary.

A flavour of what is involved can be obtained by looking at the writing rules given above and the dictionary excerpt on page 158, which are based on those of *PACE*, the controlled English used by the UK Engineering company Perkins Engines.[4] As will be clear from the dictionary excerpt, the general principle is 'one word, one meaning', for example, the only use of the verb *advise* is 'to give advice'. Thus, a usage such as *Please advise us of the availability of parts at your earliest convenience* would not be allowed, since here it means 'tell'. A useful development of such a dictionary for MT purposes would be to add information about how these words translate.

Using a restricted pool of words and terms also means that the system dictionaries can be tailored (by the MT supplier or responsible translator) to cover exactly that set of words and their translations. Being consistent about the use of terms will also help to improve the overall consistency and quality of the texts being translated.

---

[4]'PACE' stands for 'Perkins Approved Clear English'.

After all, one of the simplest and most direct benefits of MT for technical texts is that terms are always translated consistently because they are simply looked up in an electronic bilingual term dictionary.

A sample from the PACE Dictionary

advantage	n	Benefit
adverse	adj	Unfavourable
advice	n	Specialist Intelligence
advise,d	v	To provide advice
aerosol container	n	
affect,ed	v	To have an effect on
after	adv,prep	Being behind in succession, following something
again	adv	Once more
against	prep	In contact with
agglomerator	n	
agricultural	adj	Appertaining to agriculture
air	n	The gases that surround the earth
air charge cooler	n	

In general, it can be seen that the rules are mainly advice on constructions that should be avoided, usually because they lead to ambiguity. The rules for controlled languages tend to be stylistic guidelines rather than hard and fast grammar specifications. In general, much of the success of controlled languages as corporate language tools stems from the emphasis placed on critical analysis of the text and precise presentation of ideas. This is particularly apparent in the first example on page 159, which illustrates the dramatic effect of using a controlled version of English.

It is not particularly difficult to train people to write controlled language text i.e. text which generally observes some set of fairly simple writing rules. For example, the Xerox corporation currently offers its technical writers a one-day course in writing with MCE (Multinational Customised English, a Xerox proprietary language). British Aerospace teaches the rudiments of Simplified English (a general purpose technical English for the international aerospace industry) in a few fairly short training sessions.

The Effect of Using Controlled English

BEFORE:
It is equally important that there should be no seasonal changes in the procedures, as, although aircraft fuel system icing due to water contaminations more often met with in winter, it can be equally dangerous during the summer months.

AFTER:
Use the same procedure all the time, because water in the fuel system can freeze during winter or summer.

BEFORE: Loosen the dynamo or alternator mounting and adjustment link fasteners.

AFTER: Loosen the pivot fasteners of the dynamo or alternator mounting. Loosen also the fasteners of the adjustment link.

BEFORE: Reference to renewing the joints and cleaning of joint faces has to a great extent been omitted from the text, it being understood that this will be carried out where applicable.

AFTER: Normally the text does not include instructions to clean joint faces or to renew joints. These operations must be done, if necessary.

8.4 Sublanguage MT

In the previous section, we looked at a method of controlling the input to an MT system, simplifying it by avoiding certain uses of words, and avoiding potentially ambiguous constructions. Since the success of the METEO MT system, which we mentioned briefly in Chapter 1, an important strand of MT has involved concentrating on what we could loosely call 'MT for Special Purpose Languages', or sublanguage MT. Here, rather than imposing controls or simplifications on writers, one tries to exploit the restrictions in terms of vocabulary and constructions that users of the language for specialized purposes normally accept, or simply observe without reflection. The term sublanguage refers to the specialized language used (predominantly for communication between experts) in certain fields of knowledge, for example, the language of weather reports, stockmarket reports, the language of some kinds of medical discussion, the language of aeronautical engineering. Specialized vocabulary is one characteristic of such 'languages' (they typically contain words not known to the non-specialist and also words used in different or more precise ways). However sublanguages are also often characterised by special or restricted grammatical patterns. In MT, it is quite common to use the term sublanguage rather loosely to refer not just to such a specialized language, but to its use in *a particular type of text* (e.g. installation manuals, instruction booklets, diagnostic reports, learned articles), or with *a particular communicative purpose* (communication between experts, giving instructions to non-experts, etc).

The chief attraction of sublanguage and text type restriction to MT researchers is the promise of improved output, without the need to artificially restrict the input. Restricting the coverage to texts of particular types in certain subject domains will allow one to profit from regularities and restrictions in syntactic form and lexical content. This may be important enough to permit significant simplification of the architecture, and certainly leads to a reduction in the overall coverage required. We reproduce an example from English to French output from METEO:

METEO: English-French Translation

```
METRO TORONTO.
TODAY... MAINLY CLOUDY AND COLD WITH OCCASIONAL
FLURRIES. BRISK WESTERLY WINDS TO 50 KM/H. HIGH NEAR
MINUS 7.
TONIGHT... VARIABLE CLOUDINESS. ISOLATED FLURRIES.
DIMINISHING WINDS. LOW NEAR MINUS 15.
FRIDAY... VARIABLE CLOUDINESS. HIGH NEAR MINUS 6.

LE GRAND TORONTO.
AUJOURD HUI... GENERALEMENT NUAGEUX ET FROID AVEC
QUELQUES AVERSES DE NIEGE. VENTS VIFS D'OUEST A 50
KM/H. MAXIMUM D'ENVIRON MOINS 7.
CETTE NUIT ... CIEL VARIABLE. AVERSES DE NIEGE
EPARSES. AFFAIBLISSEMENT DES VENTS. MINIMUM D'ENVIRON
MOINS 15.
VENDREDI... CIEL VARIABLE. MAXIMUM D'ENVIRON MOINS
6.
```

Of course, the language of meteorological reports is special in happening to combine a rather small vocabulary with a simple, telegraphic style of writing (notice in particular the complete absence of tenses from these extracts — the few verbs there are in non-finite forms). Nonetheless, a simplification of lexical and possibly syntactic coverage can be expected in less extreme cases. To give an example with respect to lexical coverage, it is reported that 114 of the 125 occurrences of the verb *to match* in a computer software manual translate into the Japanese *icchisuru-suru*, which is listed as one of the less frequent of the 15 translations given in a small-size

English-Japanese dictionary. In the extract from a corpus of telecommunications text given below, *traffic* always corresponds to the French *trafic* and never to *circulation* (which applies only to road traffic). Moreover the dictionary writer can safely ignore the meaning of both *trafic* and *traffic* concerning dealings in illegal merchandise ('drug traffic'). Also, for an increasing number of sublanguages one can rely on the availability of a termbank (an on-line (multilingual) terminological dictionary) defining and stating equivalences for many of the technical terms that will be encountered. This greatly eases the job of dictionary construction. Such examples can be multiplied almost at will.

Extract from Telecommunications Bilingual Corpus

French:

La décision de mettre en oeuvre un nouveau système à satellites est la conséquence d'un processus à long terme qui peut être précédé des phases énumérées ci-après:

- utilisation du secteur spatial d'un système à satellites existant, généralement par location d'une certaine capacité de ce secteur;

- études économiques et techniques préliminaires de la validité et de la rentabilité d'un nouveau système, en tenant compte de la croissance du trafic et d'éventuels besoins de nouveaux services de télécommunications;

- expériences techniques et d'exploitation préliminaires, par exemple avec un satellite existant, si cela est possible, ou en lançant un satellite expérimental ou pré-opérationnel.

English:

The decision to implement a new satellite system usually results from a long term process, which may be preceded by the phases outlined below:

- Utilization of the space segment of an existing satellite system - usually by leasing space segment capacity.

- Preliminary economic and technical studies of the validity and profitability of a new system - considering the traffic growth and the possible need for new telecommunication services.

- Technical and operational preliminary experiments e.g. by using an existing satellite, if available, or even by launching an experimental or pre-operational satellite.

As for syntactic coverage, examples of instruction manuals and other forms of informative documentation typically share a number of common features. There will probably be no idioms, and a restricted set of sentential patterns. Another common feature is the relatively simple temporal dimension of the text, e.g. predominant use of the simple present. There is also the common occurrence of enumeration as a form of conjunction, usually either numbered or inset by dashes, etc. Some of these features can be seen by comparing the examples of English and French given below, which are drawn from a corpus of texts about Telecommunications. All are of great benefit to the developer or user of an MT system. For the developer, they mean that there are fewer problems of ambiguity, and development effort can be concentrated on a smaller range of constructions. For the user, this should mean that better coverage is obtained, and that the system performs better.

It is not, of course, the case that expository texts in different languages always exploit the same devices for a particular communicative purpose. The following extracts from the same corpus show that English and French differ in their use of impersonal constructions, with French favouring such constructions with the impersonal subject pronoun *il* ('it') far more in this type of text than English does. But even in these cases, it is generally easier to choose the correct translation, simply because the range of possibilities in such texts is smaller. (Literal translations of the phrases we have picked out would be: 'It is advisable to take account of...', It is manifestly much more difficult...', and 'It is advisable to take...'.)

(1) a. In this framework, the progressive evolution of the earth segment should be considered.
    Dans ce contexte, ⎡il convient de prendre en compte⎤ l'évolution progressive du secteur terrien.

(2) a. Setting up a new satellite system, which may be either a regional system with the participation of a group of countries, or a purely national (domestic) system, is obviously much more difficult than using an existing system:
    ⎡Il est manifestement beaucoup plus difficile⎤ de mettre en place un nouveau système à satellites (système régional auquel participe un groupe de pays ou système purement national) que d'utiliser un système existant:

(3) a. Simultaneously, arrangements should be made for recruitment and training of staff for installation, operation and maintenance.
    b. En même temps, ⎡il convient de prendre⎤ des dispositions pour le recrutement et la formation du personnel qui sera chargé de l'installation, de l'exploitation et de la maintenance.

Text type can strongly influence translation, not just because certain syntactic constructions are favoured (e.g. conjunction by enumeration), but also by giving special meanings to certain forms. An example of how the text type can be useful in determining translational equivalents is the translation of infinitive verb forms from French or German into English. Infinitives normally correspond to English infinitives, but are usually translated as English imperatives in instructional texts. Thus, in a printer manual one would see (4b) as the translation of (4a), rather than the literal translation.

(4)   a.   Richtige Spannung $\boxed{\text{einstellen}}$
            'correct voltage to set'

       b. $\boxed{\text{Set}}$ correct voltage

(5)   a. $\boxed{\text{Exécuter}}$ les commandes
            'to execute the commands'

       b. $\boxed{\text{Execute}}$ the commands

Thus, concentration on a sublanguage not only restricts the vocabulary and the number of source and target language constructions to be considered, it can also restrict the number of possible target translations. Given the potential that sublanguages provide for improvements in the quality of output of MT systems, and the fact that most commercial institutions do in fact have their major translation needs in restricted areas, it is not surprising that many research prototypes concentrate on restricted input in various ways, and that the design of tools and resources supporting sublanguage analysis is a major area of research.

8.5   Summary

In this chapter we have discussed three ways in which one can increase the likelihood of MT being successful by taking care with the input to the system. We first concentrated on the importance of integrating MT into the general document preparation environment, introducing the notion of the electronic document. We stressed the importance of standards in the encoding of texts, and showed how the process of MT can be aided by the adoption of the SGML markup language. In the following section, we turned to the content of texts themselves and introduced the notion of controlled languages, in which one adopts a simplified form of the language in order to communicate simply and unambiguously with the reader. Using a controlled language input greatly enhances the quality of output of MT systems. Finally we discussed sublanguage MT, or MT in restricted domains, observing that the language used in specialized technical domains is often quite different from and more restricted in style and content than the 'general language', and it is possible to take advantage of these characteristics by tailoring an MT system to the language of particular domains.

8.6   Further Reading

SGML is defined in ISO 8879, 1986, which is extensively discussed in the standard reference book on SGML[Goldfarb, 1986]. An excellent introduction to SGML is provided in [van Herwijnen, 1990].

The examples of the use of controlled language that we give in the text are based on those in [Pym, 1990]. See [Pym, 1990; Newton, 1992b] for discussion of the use of PACE as part of the translation operation in Perkins.

A noteworthy example of a controlled language is *Simplified English* (SE), which is described in the AECMA/AIA Simplified English Guide [AECMA, 1988]. This grew out of work done in the late 1970s, on behalf of the Association of European Airlines (AECMA) into readability of maintenance documentation within the civilian aircraft industry. As a result, an AECMA working group researched the procedural texts in maintenance manuals. It contains a limited general vocabulary of about 1500 words and a set of Writing Rules, similar to those we will describe above.

On sublanguage, [Arnold, 1990] provides a short overview. [Lehrberger, 1982] and [Grishman and Kittredge, 1986] are collections of articles on the subject. More detailed discussions can be found in [Kittredge, 1982], [Kittredge, 1987], [Sager, 1982], [Slocum, 1986], [Teller *et al.*, 1988] and [Hirschman, 1986].

Météo is described in [Hutchins and Somers, 1992, Chapter 12], see also [Isabelle, 1987]. Recent developments are described in [Chandioux, 1976], [Chandioux, 1989a], [Chandioux, 1989b], and [Grimaila and Chandioux, 1992].

The example concerning the English-Japanese translation of *match* in software manuals is reported in [Tsujii *et al.*, 1992].

Chapter 9

Evaluating MT Systems

9.1 Introduction

How can you tell if an MT system is 'good'? How can you tell which of two systems is 'better'? What do 'good' and 'better' mean in this context? These are the questions that this chapter tries to answer.

In a practical domain like MT, such questions reduce to questions of suitability to users' needs: what is the best and most economical way to deal with the user's translation requirements? In the ideal case, it should be possible to give a simple and straightforward answer to this question in a consumers' magazine. An article in such a magazine would discuss the most important issues with a comparison table displaying the achievements of different MT systems on tests of important aspects such as speed and quality. Unfortunately, the information necessary to make informed judgements is not so readily available, partly because the methods for investigating suitability are not well developed. In reality, MT users can spend quite a lot of money finding out what a system can and cannot do for them. In this chapter we will look at the kind of thing that should matter to potential users of MT systems, and then discuss some existing methods for assessing MT system performance.

As we pointed out in the Introduction (Chapter 1), we think that, in the short term, MT is likely to be of most benefit to largish corporate organizations doing a lot of translation. So we adopt this perspective here. However, most of the considerations apply to any potential user.

9.2 Some Central Issues

The evaluation of MT systems is a complex task. This is not only because many different factors are involved, but because measuring translation performance is itself difficult. The first important step for a potential buyer is to determine the translational needs of her organization. Therefore she needs to draw up a complete overview of the translational process, in all its different aspects. This involves establishing the size of the translation task, the text type of the material and its form (is it machine readable and if so, according to which standards). It also involves considering organizational issues, e.g. the tasks of each member of staff concerned in some way with translation. With that information at hand she can start to investigate what the consequences of the purchase of an MT system would be. These are some of the factors to keep in mind:

Organizational Changes Incorporating an MT system into the translation process will impact upon both the process and the personnel involved. There will be consequences for system administrators and support staff, but above all for the translators themselves, whose tasks will change significantly. Whereas before they will probably have spent the major part of their time actually translating or editing human translations, they will now find themselves spending a lot of time updating the system's dictionaries and post-editing the results of machine translation. There may also be a need to build automatic termbanks. Translators will need to receive training in order to perform these new tasks adequately.

It is important that the personnel support the changeover to MT. They may not always be aware of the fact that MT can lead to more job satisfaction among translators since MT systems are particularly efficient at tedious, repetitive tasks whereas more challenging translation work often still needs to be done by the human translators. If translators in an organization have decided for some reason or other that they do not want to work with MT, imposing it on them is *guaranteed* to produce poor results.

Technical environment We have emphasised right from the start that success depends in part on MT being effectively incorporated as part of a wider document preparation process inside an organization. Smooth handling of text throughout the whole process will prevent unnecessary delays. The MT engine and the document system may well come from different suppliers but they must adhere to the same standards and formats for textual material.

Bear in mind that good document preparation facilities in themselves can improve translator productivity. A decade or so ago much of the productivity increase claimed by some vendors of smaller MT systems could be attributed to their providing rather good multi-lingual word processing facilities, at a time when many translators used only an electric typewriter. Some MT vendors still supply a whole MT system package where the engine is inextricably wrapped up with some specialised word processing and text-handling tool unique to that particular system. This is undesirable on two counts: first, if you are already familiar with a good multi-lingual word processor, little is gained by having to learn another which does much the same things; second, it is likely that an MT vendor's home-grown text-processing facilities will be inferior to the best independent products, because most of the effort will have gone into developing the translation engine.

Status of Vendor Buying an MT system is a considerable investment, and the stability and future solvency of the vendor is an important consideration. After all, contact with the vendor is ideally not just limited to the initial purchase of the system. A solvent vendor can provide installation support and training in the early stages, and general support and updates later, which may improve performance considerably (e.g. specialized dictionaries, or new language pairs which can be integrated into the existing MT set-up).

Key Issues in the Evaluation of MT Systems:
The Importance of After Sales Support

Engine Performance: Speed In some circumstances, the speed at which the engine churns out raw translated text won't actually be crucial. If the system requires interaction with the translator whilst it is translating, then of course it should not amble along so slowly as to to keep the translator waiting all the time. But if it is functioning without direct interaction, it can proceed at its own pace in the background whilst the translator gets on with other jobs such as post-editing or hand translation of difficult material. This aspect also depends on the user's translational needs: if the user's material requires 15 hours daily on a fast MT system and 20 on a slower one, no one will notice the difference if the system is running overnight. Of course, there are situations where the quick delivery of translation output is essential. (The agronomist in Chapter 2, who wants to process very large quantities of material to a low level may be an example.) But in general, slow speed is the one component of MT performance of which upgrading is relatively easy: by buying some faster hardware for it to run on.

Engine Performance: Quality This is a major determinant of success. Current general purpose commercial MT systems cannot translate all texts reliably. Output can sometimes be of very poor quality indeed. We have already mentioned that the post-editing task (and with it the cost) increases as translation quality gets poorer. In the worst case, using MT could actually increase translation costs by tying up translators in editing and maintenance tasks, ultimately taking up more time than would have been required to produce translations entirely by hand. Because of its enormous influence on the overall translation cost, translation quality is a major aspect in MT evaluation.

9.3   Evaluation of Engine Performance

Substantial long-term experience with particular MT systems in particular circumstances shows that productivity improvements and cost-savings actually achieved can be very variable. Not all companies can apply MT as successfully as the following:

> In the 1980s, Perkins Engines was achieving reported cost savings of around £4000 for each diesel engine user manual translated on a PC-based WEIDNER MT system. Moreover, overall translation time per manual was more than halved from around 26 weeks to 9-12 weeks. Manuals were written in Perkins Approved Clear English (cf. Chapter 8).[Pym, 1990, pages 91-2]

Different organizations experience different results with MT. The above examples indicate that the kind of input text is one of the important factors for getting good results. A sound system evaluation is therefore one which is executed within the company itself. An MT vendor might provide you with translated material which shows what their system can do. There is, however, no guarantee that the system will do the same in a different company setting, with different texts. Only a company specific evaluation will provide the client with the feedback she ultimately wants. Information provided by the MT vendor can be useful though, e.g. if system specifications indicate what sort of text type it can or cannot handle or what sort of language constructions are problematic for their system.

In evaluating MT systems one should also take into account the fact that system performance will normally improve considerably during the first few months after its installation, as the system is tuned to the source materials, as discussed in Chapter 2. It follows that performance on an initial trial with a sample of the sort of material to be translated can only be broadly indicative of the translation quality that might ultimately be achieved after several months or years of work.

Something similar holds for those stages of the translation process which involve the translator, like dictionary updating and post-editing of the output. Times needed for these tasks will reduce as translators gain experience.

So how do we evaluate a system? Early evaluation studies were mainly concerned with the quality of MT. Of course, assessing translation quality is not just a problem for MT: it is a practical problem that human translators face, and one which translation theorists have puzzled over. For human translators, the problem is that there are typically many possible translations, some of them faithful to the original in some respects (e.g. literal meaning), while others try to preserve other properties (e.g. style, or emotional impact).[1]

In MT, the traditional transformer architecture introduces additional difficulties, since its output sentences often display structures and grammar that are unknown to the target language. It is the translator's task to find out what the correct equivalent is for the input sentence and its ill-formed translation. And, in turn, the evaluator's task is to find out how difficult the translator's task is.

In the rest of this chapter we will describe the most common evaluation methods that have been used to date and discuss their advantages and disadvantages.

9.3.1 Intelligibility

A traditional way of assessing the quality of translation is to assign scores to output sentences. A common aspect to score for is **Intelligibility**, where the intelligibility of a translated sentence is affected by grammatical errors, mistranslations and untranslated words. Some studies also take style into account, even though it does not really affect the intelligibility of a sentence. Scoring scales reflect top marks for those sentences that look like perfect target language sentences and bottom marks for those that are so badly degraded as to prevent the average translator/evaluator from guessing what a reasonable sentence might be in the context. In between

---

[1] For an excellent discussion of the range of aspects that a good translation may need to take into account, see Hatim and Mason [Hatim and Mason, 1990].

these two extremes, output sentences are assigned higher or lower scores depending on their degree of awfulness — for example, slightly fluffed word order (*"... in an interview referred Major to the economic situation..."* will probably get a better score than something where mistranslation of words has rendered a sentence almost uninterpretable (*"...the peace contract should take off the peace agreement...."*). Thus scoring for intelligibility reflects directly the quality judgment of the user; the less she understands, the lower the intelligibility score. Therefore it might seem a useful measure of translation quality.

Is there any principled way of constructing an intelligibility scoring system? Or rather is there any generally agreed, and well motivated scoring system? We do not know of any. The major MT evaluation studies which have been published report on different scoring systems; the number of points on the scoring scales ranging from 2 (intelligible, unintelligible) to 9. The 9 point scale featured in the famous ALPAC Report and was not just used to score the intelligibility of MT, but also of human translation. As a consequence the scale included judgments on fairly subtle differences in e.g. style. This scale is relatively well-defined and well-tested. Nevertheless we think that it is too fine-grained for MT evaluation and leads to an undesirable dispersion of scoring results. Also, we think that style should not be included because it does not affect the intelligibility of a text. On the other hand, a two point scale does not give us enough information on the seriousness of those errors which affect the intelligibility. (A two point scale would not allow a distinction to be drawn between the examples in the previous paragraph, and complete garbage, (or something completely untranslated) and a fully correct translation.) Perhaps a four point scale like the one below would be more appropriate.

An Example Intelligibility Scale

1 The sentence is perfectly clear and intelligible. It is grammatical and reads like ordinary text.

2 The sentence is generally clear and intelligible. Despite some inaccuracies or infelicities of the sentence, one can understand (almost) immediately what it means.

3 The general idea of the sentence is intelligible only after considerable study. The sentence contains grammatical errors and/or poor word choices.

4 The sentence is unintelligible. Studying the meaning of the sentence is hopeless; even allowing for context, one feels that guessing would be too unreliable.

Once devised, scoring scales need to be tested, to make sure that scale descriptions are clear and do not contain any expression that can be interpreted differently by different evaluators. The test procedure should be repeated until the scale descriptions are uniformly interpreted by evaluators.

A reasonable size group of evaluators/scorers must be used to score the MT output. Four scorers is the minimum; a bigger group would make the results more reliable. The scorers should be familiar with the subject area of the text they will score and their knowledge of the source language of the translation should also be good. Before an official scoring session is held the scorers participate in a training session in which they can become acquainted with the scale description. This training session should be similar for all scorers. During scoring it should be impossible to refer to the source language text.

9.3.2 Accuracy

By measuring intelligibility we get only a partial view of translation quality. A highly intelligible output sentence need not be a correct translation of the source sentence. It is important to check whether the meaning of the source language sentence is preserved in the translation. This property is called **Accuracy** or **Fidelity**. Scoring for accuracy is normally done in combination with (but after) scoring for intelligibility.

As with intelligibility, some sort of scoring scheme for accuracy must be devised. Whilst it might initially seem tempting to just have simple 'Accurate' and 'Inaccurate' labels, this could be somewhat unfair to an MT system which routinely produces translations which are only slightly deviant in meaning. Such a system would be deemed just as inaccurate as an automated 'Monty Python' phrasebook which turns the innocent request *Please line my pockets with chamois* [2] into the target language statement *My hovercraft is full of eels*. Obviously enough, if the output sentence is complete gobbledegook (deserving of the lowest score for intelligibility) then it is impossible to assign a meaning, and so the question of whether the translation means the same as the original cannot really be answered. (Hence accuracy testing follows intelligibility rating).

The evaluation procedure is fairly similar to the one used for the scoring of intelligibility. However the scorers obviously have to be able to refer to the source language text (or a high quality translation of it in case they cannot speak the source language), so that they can compare the meaning of input and output sentences.

As it happens, in the sort of evaluation considered here, accuracy scores are much less interesting than intelligibility scores. This is because accuracy scores are often closely related to the intelligibility scores; high intelligibility normally means high accuracy. Most of the time most systems don't exhibit surreal or Monty Python properties. For some purposes it might be worth dispensing with accuracy scoring

---

[2] This comes from the section on 'Talking to the Tailor' in an English-Italian phrasebook of the 1920s.

altogether and simply counting cases where the output looks silly (leading one to suppose something has gone wrong).

It should be apparent from the above that devising and assigning quality scores for MT output — what is sometimes called 'Static' or 'Declarative Evaluation'[3] — is not straightforward. Interpreting the resultant scores is also problematic.

It is virtually impossible — even for the evaluator — to decide what a set of intelligibility and accuracy scores for a single MT system might mean in terms of cost-effectiveness as a 'gisting' device or as a factor in producing high quality translation. To see this, consider the sort of quality profile you might get as a result of evaluation (Figure 9.1), which indicates that most sentences received a score of 3 or 4, hence of middling intelligibility. Does that mean that you can use the system to successfully gist agricultural reports? One cannot say.

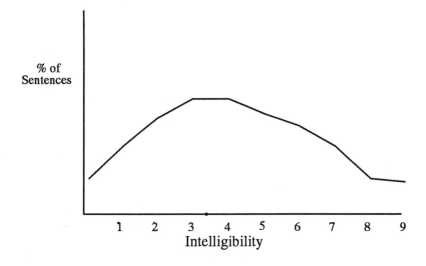

Figure 9.1 Typical Quality Profile for an MT System

Turning to the high-quality translation case, it is clear that substantial post-editing will be required. But it is not clear — without further information about the relationship between measured quality and post-editing times — what effect on overall translator productivity the system will have. Whilst it is presumably true that increasingly unintelligible sentences will tend to be increasingly difficult to post-edit, the relationship may not be linear. For example, it may be that sorting out minor problems (which don't affect intelligibility very much) is just as much of an editing problem as correcting mistranslations of words (which affect intelligibility

---

[3]'Declarative' here is to be contrasted with 'procedural'. A declarative specification of a program states what the program should do, without considering the order in which it must be done. A procedural specification would specify both what is to be done, and when. Properties like Accuracy and Intelligibility are properties of a system which are independent of the dynamics of the system, or the way the system operates at all — hence 'non-procedural', or 'declarative'.

a great deal). We could for example imagine the following two sentences to be part of our sample text in Chapter 2. The first one is more intelligible than the second, yet more time will be needed to fix the errors in it:

(1) a.   The print☐ page should be │from│ excell│ing│ quality,

     b.   The printed page should │his │ excellent quality.

It is true that a comparative evaluation of a number of different MT systems might demonstrate that one system is in all respects better than the others. The information however does not tell us whether buying the better MT system will improve the total translation process — the system could still be unprofitable. And even if two particular systems have different performance profiles, it may not always be clear whether one profile is likely to be better matched to the task in hand than the other. For example, look at the intelligibility ratings for systems A and B in Figure 9.2. For system A the majority of sentences are neither very good nor bad (rating 3 or 4). System B, by comparison, tends to do either quite well (scores of 7 are common) or quite badly (scores 1, and 2 are frequent). Which system will be better in practice? It is not possible to say.

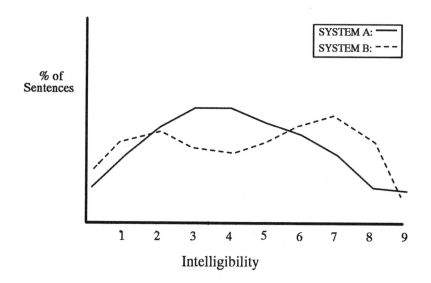

Figure 9.2 Which Performance Curve is Better?

9.3.3   Error Analysis

Rather than using broad indicators as guides to score assignments, you could focus on the errors the MT system makes. The technique of error analysis tries to establish how seriously errors affect the translation output.

The method is this. To start off, write down a large list of all the types of errors you think the MT system might make. During the evaluation, all the errors in the translated text are counted up. Because you consider some errors more serious than others, each type of error will be multiplied by some *weighting factor* which you assign to it. The score then for each individual sentence or the whole text will be the sum of all the weighted errors. So, if we take the raw translation we were using in the scenario in Chapter 2 as an example, error analysis might work as follows.

For the example three sorts of error are identified. These three sorts are errors involving selection of *a* vs *one* as the translation of German *ein*, errors in number agreement (e.g. **a computers*), and errors in the selection of prepositions. Using some short codes for each error type, each error occurrence is marked up in the raw output. The resulting marked text is given below.

Markup of Errors

Adjustment of the print density:

- Turn the button an $\boxed{\text{A/ONE}}$ or two positions in direction of the dark indicator.

- Switch off the printer for a moment and then again a $\boxed{\text{PREP}}$, so that the test page is printed.

- Repeat the two previous steps as long as, until you see Gray on the background of the page, similarly like at $\boxed{\text{PREP}}$ easily unclean copies of a photocopier.

- Turn back the button a position.

Now you can connect the printer to the computer.

If you connect the printer to a Macintosh computers $\boxed{\text{NUM}}$, continue with the instructions in the chapter 3. If you use an other computer, continue with chapters $\boxed{\text{NUM}}$ 4.

To calculate the seriousness of the errors, weights in the range 0 to 1 are assigned to the three error types. The weight for an error in preposition selection is higher than that for incorrect number because the person responsible considers that incorrect number is relatively less serious. This is summarized in the following table.

ERROR TYPE	WEIGHT
a/one selection	0.4
Number	0.2
Preposition	0.6

On the basis of this the total error score can be calculated. There are two errors in NUMber agreement, two involving PREPositions, and one involving A/ONE selection, so the score is: $(2 \times 0.2) + (2 \times 0.6) + (1 \times 0.4) = 2$

Although this method gives more direct information on the usefulness of an MT system, there are immediate problems with using detailed error analysis. The first is practical: it will usually require considerable time and effort to train scorers to identify instances of particular errors — and they will also need to spend more time analysing each output sentence. Second, is there any good basis for choosing a particular weighting scheme? Not obviously. The weighting is in some cases related to the consequences an error has for post-editing: how much time it will take to correct that particular mistake. In some other cases it merely reflects how badly an error affects the intelligibility of the sentence. Consequently, the result will either indicate the size of the post-editing task or the intelligibility of the text, with its relative usefulness. In both cases devising a weighting scheme will be a difficult task.

There is, however, a third problem and perhaps this is the most serious one: for some MT systems, many output sentences are so corrupted with respect to natural language correlates that detailed analysis of errors is not meaningful. Error types are not independent of each other: failure to supply any number inflection for a main verb will often mean that the subject and verb do not agree in number as required. It will be difficult to specify where one error starts and another ends and thus there is the risk of ending up with a general error scale of the form *one, two, ... lots*. The assignment of a weighting to such complex errors is thus a tricky business.

9.3.4   The Test Suite

As we noted before, for some years the trend (at least in research circles) has been towards Translation Engines with substantial linguistic knowledge in the form of grammars. LK Engines have a different performance profile from Transformer Engines in that their output will tend to contain rather fewer badly degraded sentences. (Perhaps at the price of failing to produce *anything* in some cases).

Although the use of linguistic-knowledge based techniques tends to promote higher Intelligibility (and Accuracy) output, it is possible that the linguistic knowledge embedded in the system is defective or incomplete. Sometimes a certain grammar rule is too strict or too general to apply correctly in all circumstances; sometimes the rules that handle one phenomenon (e.g. modal verbs like *may* in *The printer may fail*) and the rules that handle another phenomenon (eg. negation) fail to work correctly together when the two phenomena co-occur or interact in a sentence. (For example, imagine the problems that will result if *The printer can not be cleaned* (i.e. can be left uncleaned), and *The printer cannot be cleaned* (i.e. must not be cleaned) are confused.)

Keeping track of these sorts of constructional errors and deficits has become rather a severe problem for developers of MT systems and other large NLP systems. For example, while running the system on a corpus of test texts will reveal many problems, many potential areas of difficulty are hidden because the statistics are such that even quite large corpora will lack even a single example of particular grammatical combinations of linguistic phenomena.

Rather than churning through increasingly large 'natural' text corpora, developers have recently turned their attention to the use of suites of specially constructed test sentences. Each sentence in the suite contains either one linguistic construction of interest or a combination thereof. Thus part of an English test suite might look as follows.

Extract from a Test Suite

John runs.	
John will run.	*modal auxiliaries*
John can run.	
John may run.	
John should run.	
John could run.	
John does not run.	*negation (with do-support)*
John not run.	
John will not run	*negation and modal auxiliaries.*
John can not run.	
John may not run.	
John should not run.	
John could not run.	
....	

This fragment just churns through all combinations of modal verbs like *can, may* together with optional *not*. In practice, one would expect test suites to run to very many thousands of sentences, because of the many different combinations of grammatical phenomena that can occur. Suites may include grammatically unacceptable sentences (e.g. *John not run) which the parser should recognize as incorrect. In systems which use the same linguistic knowledge for both analysing and synthesising text, the fact that an ill-formed sentence is rejected in analysis suggests that it is unlikely to be constructed in synthesis either.

Nobody knows for sure how test suites should be constructed and used in MT. A bi-directional system (a system that not only translates from German to English *and* from English to German) will certainly need test suites for both languages. Thus success in correctly translating all the sentences in a German test suite into English and all the sentences in an English test suite into German would definitely be encouraging. However, standard test suites are rather blunt instruments for probing translation performance in the sense that they tend to ignore typical differences between the languages involved in translation.

We can look at an example. In English the perfect tense is expressed with the auxiliary verb *have*, like in *He has phoned*. In German however there are two auxiliary verbs for perfect tense: *haben* and *sein*. Which verb is used depends on the main verb of the sentence: most require the first, some require the second. So an English and a German test suite designed to check the handling of perfect tense will look different.

Part of English-German Test Suite

English:
....
He has phoned.
He had phoned.
...

German:
....
Er ist gegangen.	*sein*
Er hat angerufen.	*haben*
Er war gegangen.	*sein*
Er hatte angerufen.	*haben*
...

The German test suite thus tests the perfect tense for verbs that take *sein* and verbs that take *haben* and therefore have to test twice the number of sentences to test the same phenomenon. However, if *He has phoned* is correctly translated into German *Er hat angerufen*, then we still can not be sure that all perfect tenses are translated correctly. For testing of the English grammar alone, there is no reason to include a sentence like *He has gone* into the English test suite, since the perfect tense has already been tested. For translation into German however it would be interesting to see whether the auxiliary verb sein is selected by the main verb *gehen*, giving the correct translation *Er ist gegangen.*

Given this sort of problem, it is clear that monolingual test suites should be supplemented with further sentences in each language designed to probe specific language pair differences. They could probably be constructed by studying data which has traditionally been presented in books on comparative grammar.[4]

In a bi-directional system, we need test suites for both languages involved *and* test suites probing known translational problems between the two languages. Constructing test suites is a very complicated task, since they need to be complete with regard to the phenomena occurring in the present and future input texts of the MT user. Thus one should first check whether there are any existing test suites for the languages that need to be tested. (There are several monolingual test suites around). Such a suite can be modified by adding material and removing restrictions that are irrelevant in the texts for which the system is intended (eg. the texts to be translated might not contain any questions). As far as we know there are no readily available test suites for translational problems between two languages; to test for this, the evaluator will have to adapt existing monolingual ones.

Once the test suites have been devised they are run through the system and an inventory of errors is compiled. Clearly the test suite is an important tool in MT system development. How useful will it be for a *user* of MT systems?

It is of course possible for the user to run an MT system on a test suite of her own devising and, in some cases, this may be perfectly appropriate. It is especially useful to measure improvements in a system when the MT vendor provides a system update. However, the test suite approach does entail some drawbacks when used to assess system performance in comparison with competing systems. The problem is familiar by now: how are the evaluation results to be interpreted? Suppose System A and System B both produce acceptable translations for 40% of the test sentences and that they actually fail on different, or only partially overlapping, subsets of sentences. Which one is better? If System B (but not System A) fails on test sentences which embody phenomena with very low frequencies in the user's type of text material, then clearly System B is the better choice. But users typically do not have reliable information on the relative frequencies of various types of constructions in their material, and it is a complex task to retrieve such information by going through texts manually (automated tools to do the job are not yet widely available).

The same problem of interpretability holds when MT systems are evaluated by an independent agency using some sort of standard set of test suites. Published test suite information certainly gives a much better insight into expected performance than the vague promisory notes offered with current systems; but it doesn't im-

---

[4]It would be nice to try to find possible problem areas by some sort of automatic scanning of bilingual texts but the tools and techniques are not available to date.

mediately translate into information about likely performance in practice, or about cost effectiveness.

On top of this there is the problem of how to design a test suite, and the cost of actually constructing it. Research is ongoing to determine what sort of sentences should go into a test suite: which grammatical phenomena should be tested and to what extent should one include co-occurrence of grammatical phenomena, should a test suite contain sentences to test semantic phenomena and how does one test translation problems? These and additional problems might be solved in the future, resulting in proper guidelines for test suite construction.

9.4 Operational Evaluation

In the previous sections we have discussed various types of quality assessment. One mayor disadvantage of quality assessment for MT evaluation purposes, however, is the fact the overall performance of an MT system has to be judged on more aspects than translation quality only. The most complete and direct way to determine whether MT performs well in a given set of circumstances is to carry out an operational evaluation on site comparing the combined MT and post-editing costs with those associated with pure human translation. The requirement here is that the vendor allows the potential buyer to test the MT system in her particular translation environment. Because of the enormous investment that buying a system often represents, vendors should allow a certain test period. During an operational evaluation a record is kept of all the user's costs, the translation times and other relevant aspects. This evaluation technique is ideal in the sense that it gives the user direct information on how MT would fit in and change the existing translation environment and whether it would be profitable.

Before starting up the MT evaluation the user should have a clear picture of the costs that are involved in the current set-up with human translation. When this information on the cost of the current translation service is available the MT experiment can begin.

In an operational evaluation of MT time plays an important role. Translators need to be paid and the more time they spend on post-editing MT output and updating the system's dictionaries, the less profitable MT will be. In order to get a realistic idea of the time needed for such translator tasks they need to receive proper training prior to the experiment. Also, the MT system needs to be tuned towards the texts it is supposed to deal with.

During an evaluation period lasting several months it should be possible to fully cost the use of MT, and at the end of the period, comparison with the costs of human translation should indicate whether, in the particular circumstances, MT would be profitable in financial terms or not.

One problem is that though one can compare cost in this way, one does not necessarily hold quality constant. For example, it is sometimes suspected that post-edited MT translations tend to be of inferior quality to pure human translations because there is some temptation to post-edit only up to that point where a correct (rather than good) translation is realised. This would mean that cost benefits of MT might have to be set against a fall in quality of translation. There are several ways to deal with this. One could e.g. use the quality measurement scales described above (Section 9.3.1). In this case we would need a fine-grained scale like in the ALPAC Report, since the differences between post-edited MT and HT will be small. But what does this quality measurement mean in practice? Do we have to worry about slight differences in quality if after all an 'acceptable' translation is produced? Maybe a better solution would be to ask an acceptability judgment from the customer. If the customer notices a quality decrease which worries him, then clearly post-editing quality needs to be improved. In most cases, however, the experienced translator/post-editor is more critical towards translation quality than the customer is.

In general it seems an operational evaluation conducted by a user will be extremely expensive, requiring 12 personmonths or more of translator time. An attractive approach is to integrate the evaluation process in the normal production process, the only difference being that records are kept on the number of input words, the turnaround time and the costs in terms of time spent in post-editing. The cost of such an integrated operational evaluation is obviously less. After all, if the system is really good the translation costs will have been reduced and will compensate for some of the costs of the evaluation method. (On the other hand, if the system is not an improvement for the company, the money spent on its evaluation will be lost of course.)

9.5   Summary

The purchase of an MT system is in many cases a costly affair and requires careful consideration. It is important to understand the organizational consequences and to be aware of the system's capacities. Unfortunately, it is not possible to draw up a comparison table for MT systems on the basis of which MT buyers could choose their system. Although system specifications can provide us with some useful information there are too many aspects which influence the performance of MT that cannot be included in such a table. Furthermore, MT will perform differently in different translation environments, depending mainly on the character of the typical input texts. Without having the necessary information of the kind of input texts the user has in mind, it is not possible to make a reliable prediction about the cost effectiveness of an MT system. The consequences are that if we want information about an MT system we have to evaluate it, and that this evaluation has to be specifically for the user's translational needs.

The evaluation strategies discussed in this chapter are strategies that a buyer might want to pursue when considering the purchase of an MT system. Although they will provide the client with a certain amount of useful information, each method has some drawbacks, which we have tried to point out in our discussion.

9.6 Further Reading

Useful discussion of evaluation methods can be found in [van Slype, 1982], and [Lehrberger and Bourbeau, 1987]. Practical discussion of many different aspects of MT evaluation can be found in [King and Falkedal, 1990], [Guida and Mauri, July 1986], and [Balkan et al., 1991].

A special issue of the Journal *Machine Translation* is dedicated to issues of evaluation of MT (and other NLP) systems. The introduction to the issue, [Arnold et al., in press b], gives an overview of the state of the issues involved, going into more detail about some issues glossed over here. Several of the articles which appear in this issue report practical experience of evaluation, and suggest techniques (for example, [Albisser, in press; Flank et al., in press; Jordan, in press; Neal et al., in press].)

The problems of focusing evaluation on the MT engine itself (i.e. apart from surrounding peripherals) are discussed in [Krauwer, in press].

As things stand, evaluating an MT system (or other NLP system) involves a great deal of human activity, in checking output, for example. A method for automating part of the evaluation process is described in [Shiwen, in press].

Some of the issues involved in construction of test suites are discussed in [Arnold et al., in press a], and [Nerbonne et al., in press].

In this chapter, we have generally taken the users' perspective. However, evaluation is also an essential for system developers (who have to be able to guage whether, and how much, their efforts are improving a system). How evaluation technique can be applied so as to aid developers discussed in [Minnis, in press].

One of the best examples of MT evaluation in terms of rigour was that which formed the basis of the ALPAC report [Pierce and Carroll, 1966], which we mentioned in Chapter 1 (it is normal to be rude about the conclusions of the ALPAC report, but this should not reflect on the evaluation on which the report was based: the evaluation itself was a model of care and rigour — it is the interpretation of the results for the potential of MT which was regrettable).

See [Nagao, 1986, page 59] for more detailed scales and criteria for evaluating fidelity and ease of understanding.

As usual, Hutchins and Somers [Hutchins and Somers, 1992] contains a useful discussion of evaluation issues (Chapter 9).

Chapter 10

New Directions in MT

10.1 Introduction

In the previous chapters, we have tried to give an idea of what is currently possible in MT. In this chapter, we look to the future. Our aim is to give a flavour of current research in MT, indicating what issues are receiving attention and what techniques are thought to be promising.

Of course, not all the ideas that are currently important are really *new* ones. A great deal of current research is directed at how familiar techniques can be improved — for example, how standard 'Linguistic Knowledge'approaches can be improved by using better linguistic analyses (analyses based on better linguistic theories, or a better understanding of existing theories), and developing or adapting more efficient processing methods, and better tools for use in constructing and modifying systems. Likewise, an important feature of current research involves work on sublanguage MT (cf. Chapter 8), but though the design of tools to aid sublanguage analysis is an increasingly important area, it is hardly a new development. Other currently important work is concerned with *integration*, which can relate either to the integration of MT with other Natural Language Processing technologies, or to the (non-trivial) problems of integration of MT into general document processing technology that arise as one tries to make a practically and commercially usable system out of a research prototype MT system. A particularly important example of the former is research on 'speech-to-speech' MT systems — that is, systems that can take spoken input, and produce spoken output (e.g. for more or less simultaneous interpreting of telephone conversations). Such work is clearly important, and often throws up interesting differences of emphasis (for example, in speech-to-speech work, there is an emphasis on speed, and on dealing with sentence fragments, since one would like to be able to translate each utterance as it is spoken, without waiting for the end. This gives importance to 'bottom up' methods of analysis, and severe restrictions on the input in terms of text-type, etc). However, there is an obvious sense in which such work it is 'more of the same' — it involves improving one aspect of an existing idea, rather than presenting a genuinely new direction, and would be accessible on the basis of the earlier chapters of this book. In this chapter, we will concentrate on what we think may turn out to be more radical ideas.

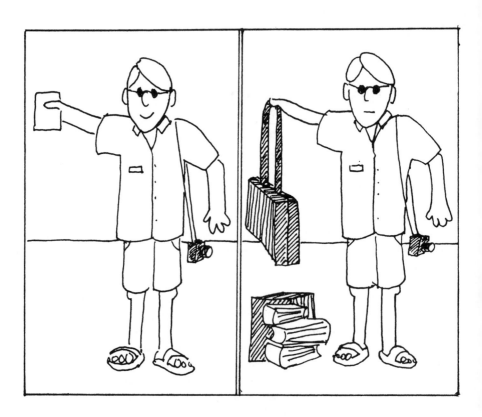

The Impact of Technology No. 58: Machine Translation and Tourism.
The Super Mini Etrans Tourist Translation System replaces the old fashioned Phrase Book. It comes complete with integrated laptop computer, carrying case, power pack, and 3 volumes of documentation.

The chapter has three main sections. In Section 10.2, we outline some current issues and trends in the design of sets of linguistic rules for MT, that is, work within the established 'Linguistic Knowledge', or 'Rule-Based' paradigm. The next section (10.3) gives an overview of some of the corpus and machine readable dictionary resources which have recently become available. These resources have stimulated a great deal of research within the traditional LK/rule-based paradigm, and have also been of key importance in the trend towards so-called *empirical* approaches to MT, which are sketched in Section 10.4.

10.2 Rule-Based MT

10.2.1 Flexible or Multi-level MT

Most transfer or interlingual rule-based systems are based on the idea that success in practical MT involves defining a level of representations for texts which is abstract enough to make translation itself straightforward, but which is at the same time superficial enough to permit sentences in the various source and target languages to be successfully mapped into that level of representation. That is, successful MT involves a compromise between depth of analysis or understanding of the source text, and the need to actually compute the abstract representation. In this sense, transfer systems are less ambitious than interlingual systems, because they accept the need for (often quite complex) mapping rules between the most abstract representations of source and target sentences. As our linguistic knowledge increases, so too MT systems based on linguistic rules encoding that knowledge should improve. This position is based on the fundamental assumption that finding a sufficiently abstract level of representation for MT is an attainable goal. However, some researchers have suggested that it is not always the case that the deepest level of representation is necessarily the best level for translation.

This can be illustrated easily by thinking about translation between closely related languages such as Norwegian and Swedish.

(1) a. Min nya bil är blå(Swedish)
          'my new car is blue'

      b. Den nye bilen min er blå(Norwegian)
          'the new car mine is blue'

(2) a. Var har du hittat en såful slips? (Swedish)
          'Where did you find a such ugly tie'

      b. Hvor har du funnet et såstygt slips? (Norwegian)
          'Where did you find a such ugly tie'

In the second example here, both languages have exactly the same word order, although the words themselves and their grammatical features differ. In the first example, we see that Swedish (like English) does not allow the use of an article together with a possessive pronoun, which Norwegian (like, say, Italian) does. These are certainly minimal differences, and it would be a serious case of overkill to subject the source language sentences to 'in depth' analysis, when essentially all that is required to deal with this structural difference is to express a correspondence between the structures described by the following syntactic rules (here 'Poss' stands for 'Possessive pronoun').

(Swedish) NP → Poss Adj N

(Norwegian) NP → Det Adj N Poss

Of course, it would be straightforward to design a special purpose MT system which was equipped only with the sort of linguistic rules required to perform this type of superficial manipulation of syntactic structures. But a number of considerations, not least economic considerations, militate against this. Instead one could conclude that what is required is an approach to rule-based translation which is sufficiently *flexible* to carry out deep analysis only when required, so that the same MT engine can be used for dealing with pairs of closely related languages and pairs of languages which differ greatly. Such ideas lie behind attempts to design flexible systems which can operate in a variety of modes, according to the depth of analysis required for the language pair, or even the particular examples in hand.

There are other reasons for the current interest in flexible systems. In the example above, we have tried to show that what is the 'appropriate level' of analysis for one language pair might be quite inappropriate for another pair. But some researchers have pointed out that a similar situation obtains within one and the same language pair. Though really convincing arguments are hard to find, the idea is that translation seems to depend on information about different levels of linguistic information at the same time. For example, for most translation purposes, as we have noted previously, a representation in terms of semantic relations (AGENT, PATIENT, etc.) is attractive. However, such a representation will probably not distinguish between (2a), (2b) and (2c). This means they will be translated alike, if this is the representation that is produced by analysis. But in many cases this would not produce a very good translation.

(3)   a.   Sam broke the printer.

     b.   It was the printer that Sam broke.

     c.   It was Sam that broke the printer

Ideally, what one wants is a semantic account of the differences between these examples. This has to do with the difference between what is presupposed, and what is asserted, or what is treated as 'given', and what as new information (e.g. in (3b) it is presupposed that Sam broke something, and stated that the thing in question was the printer). Producing such an account is not impossible, and may indeed produce a better MT system in the long run. However, it is by no means easy, and, at least in the short term, it would be nice if one could use information about semantic relations where that is useful, and information about surface syntactic form where that was useful. This would be possible if one had a way of allowing information from a variety of levels to be referred to in transfer. Of course, the difficulty then would be to allow this flexibility while still ensuring that the pieces of information can be correctly combined to give a suitable target translation.

There are various proposals in the MT literature concerning flexible MT. Some researchers working within the paradigm of example-based MT, which we discuss below, have proposed architectures which are flexible with respect to the level at which translation occurs. Another rather radical idea depends on the fact that several contemporary linguistic theories provide a 'multidimensional' characterisation of a linguistic string. One can get a flavour of what is involved by looking at the following representation.

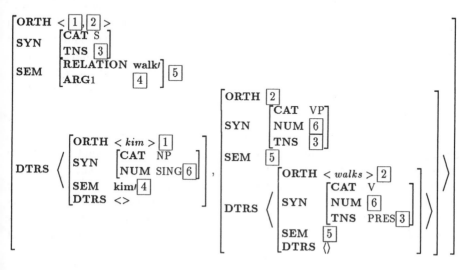

Figure 10.1 A Multidimensional Representation

This representation of the sentence *Kim walks* is multidimensional, in the sense that it contains information about several levels, or dimensions, of structure at the same time: information about ORTHography, SYNtax, SEMantics, and constituent structure (the DaughTeRs feature). Such multidimensional representations are known as **signs**. Identity of values is indicated by tags, boxed indices like [1], [2].

If we look first at the DTRS value, we can see that there are two daughters, the first an NP (i.e. whose SYNtax contains an attribute CAT with value NP), and the second a VP. The NP has no daughters, and the VP has one daughter, whose category is V. The ORTHography of the whole S is made up of [1], the ORTHography of the NP, i.e. *mary*, and the ORTHography of the VP, which is identical to the ORTHography of the V, tagged [2]. The TNS (TeNSe) of S, VP, and V are identical, and the NP, VP, and V have the same NUMber value.

The semantics of the S indicates that the argument of the predicate **walk/** is the value tagged [4], that is, the semantics of the NP, **mary/**.

We have seen that representation carries information about ORTHography, SYN-Tax, SEMantics and daughters (DTRS) at the same time (a fuller representation would include information about morphology too). Formally, it is just a collection of features (i.e. attributes and values) of the kind we have seen before, with the difference that the value of some of the attributes can be an entire structure (collection of features), and we allow different attributes to have the same value (indicated by means of a **tag**, a number written in a box). This is sometimes called a re-entrance.[1]

The syntactic information is essentially equivalent to the sorts of category label we have seen before, and the value of the DTRS attribute simply gives the values of the daughters a node would have in a normal consituent structure tree of the kind that were given in Chapter 3. One interesting point to note is that there is a value for SEMantics given for the mother sign, and for every one of the daughter signs. (In fact, the SEM value of the S is identical to the SEM value of the VP, and the V, and the SEM value of the AGENT of the S is identical to the SEM value of the NP *Kim*.)

One way one could use such a structure would be just to take the value of the SEM attribute for the mother sign in the output of analysis, and input this value to transfer (in a transfer system) or synthesis (in an interlingual system). This would involve only adapting the techniques we described in earlier chapters for transfer and synthesis to deal with complex attribute-value structures, rather than trees (this is not very difficult). Of course, this would mean that one was losing any benefit of multidimensionality for translation (though one might be able to exploit it in analysis).

If one is to exploit multidimensionality in transfer or synthesis (which was the aim) the only possible part of the sign to recurse through, applying rules, is the structure of the DTRS attribute. However, as we noted, this is just the surface phrase structure, enhanced with some information about semantics and orthography. If this is so, then one might wonder whether any advantage has been gained at all.

The solution is not to think in terms of applying rules to representations or structures at all, but to focus on the attribute-value structure as simply a convenient graphic representation of the solution to a set of constraints. For example, for the representation on page 187, one such constraint would be that the CATegory value of the mother sign is S. More precisely, the value of SYN on the mother sign is an attribute-value structure which contains an attribute CAT, with value S. That is, if we give names like X0, X1, X2, etc. to the various attribute-value structures, with X0 the name of the mother sign, then the value of SYN in X0 is a structure X1, and the value of CAT in X1 is S:

```
X0:SYN = X1
```

[1]Here 'same value' is to be interpreted strongly, as *token* identity — in a sentence with two nouns, there would be two objects with the 'same' category value, namely, the two nouns. This is often called 'type' identity. In everyday usage, when we speak of two people having the 'same' shirt, we normally mean type identity. Token identity would involve them sharing one piece of clothing. On the other hand, when we speak of people having the same father, we mean token identity.

```
X1:CAT = S
```

If we name the attribute-value structure of the VP X4, and that of the V X5, we also have the following, indicating that S, VP, and V all have the same SEM values.

```
X0:SEM = X4:SEM

X4:SEM = X5:SEM
```

The value of the ORTHography attribute in X0 is the concatenation of the values in the NP (X6) and the VP (X5):

```
X0:ORTH = concatenation(X6:ORTH, X5,ORTH)
```

One can think of a representation like that on page 187 as simply a graphic representation of the solution to a set of such equations, and one can use the equations as the basis for translation, in the following way. First, it is the task of analysis to produce the equation set. This is not, in fact, difficult — we have already seen, in Chapter 3 how one can add instructions to grammar rules to create different kinds of representations. Using them to create sets of equations is a simple extension of this idea. This set of constraints describes a source structure. The translation problem is now to produce a set of constraints whose solution will yield a target language structure. Ultimately, of course, one is interested in the ORTH value in such a structure, but in the meantime, one can state constraints such as: "the SEM of the source structure, and the SEM of the target structure must be identical" (this assumes that the SEM values are 'interlingual'), or "the SEM of the target structure must be the result of applying some 'transfer' function to the SEM of the source structure". But one can easily state constraints in terms of other attributes, for example, "in the case of proper nouns, the value of ORTH in the source structure and the value of ORTH in the target structure must be the same". Similarly, if we add attributes and values giving information about grammatical relations such as subject, etc. into the constraints, we can state constraints in terms of these.

Of course, we cannot, in this way, guarantee that we will deal with all of the source structure (we may leave parts untranslated by failing to produce appropriate target language constraints), or that solving the target language constraints will produce a single target structure, or even any structure at all (the constraints may be inconsistent). Nor have we indicated *how* the constraints are to be solved. Moreover, one will often not want such constraints to be observed absolutely, but only by default. For example, proper names should only keep the same orthography form if there is no constraint that says otherwise (in translating English into French, one would like to ensure that *London* translates as *Londres*). There are a number of serious difficulties and open research questions here. However, one can get a feeling for a partial solution to some of these problems by considering the following rather simple approach.

Recall that the constraints we gave above made the SEMantics of the S equal to the SEMantics of the VP, and the V. One may immediately think of this as involving the V contributing its SEMantics to the S, but one can also see it the other way round, as putting the semantics of the whole S 'into' the V. What this means, of course, is that all the semantic information conveyed by the sentence is represented (somewhat redundantly) in the representations of the words. Now suppose that we have translation constraints which say, for example, that the translation of the word *walk* must be the word *marcher*, with the same semantics, and that the translation of *Sam* must be *Sam*, again with the same semantics. What we must do now is produce a target structure. The problem we have is interestingly like the problem we have when we try to parse a sentence: then we typically know what the words are, and what order they are in, but not what the sentence as a whole means; here we know what the words are, and what the sentence as a whole means (it is represented 'in the words'), but not what the word order should be. One possibility is simply to use the target grammar to parse *Sam*, and *marcher* in all possible orders. To take a slightly more interesting case, suppose the source sentence is (3):

(4)   Sam sees London.

If the target language is French, the target grammar will be asked to parse the strings in (4):

(5)   a.   *voit Sam Londres.

       b.   ?Londres voit Sam.

       c.   *Sam Londres voit.

       d.   Sam voit Londres.

One can expect the target grammar to reject (5a), and (5c). It would accept (5b), but only with the meaning that is different from that of the source sentence, which we have carried over in the constraints linking *see* to *voir*. This leaves only the correct solution (5d).

10.2.2   Knowledge-Based MT

The term *knowledge-based MT* has come to describe a rule-based system displaying extensive semantic and pragmatic knowledge of a domain, including an ability to reason, to some limited extent, about concepts in the domain (the components, installation and operation of a particular brand of laser printer could constitute a domain). We noted the appeal of such an approach as a way of solving some basic MT problems in earlier chapters. Essentially, the premise is that high quality translation requires in-depth understanding of the text, and the development of the *domain model* would seem to be necessary to that sort of deep understanding. One of the important considerations driving this work is an appreciation that post-editing is time-consuming and very expensive, and therefore that efforts made to produce high quality output will pay off in the long run. Since this may well turn out to be of great utility, in this section we concentrate on an approach which attempts some degree of text understanding on the basis of detailed domain knowledge, developed at the Center for Machine Translation at Carnegie Mellon University in Pittsburgh.

To give some idea of what is at stake here, the prototype systems developed for English ↔ Japanese translation during the late 1980s at CMU, dealing with the translation of instruction manuals for personal computers, contained the following components:

- an ontology of concepts

- analysis lexica and grammars for English and Japanese

- generation lexica and grammars for English and Japanese

- mapping rules between the Interlingua and English/Japanese syntax

For a small vocabulary (around 900 words), some 1500 concepts were defined in detail. The ontology dealt solely with the interaction between personal computers and their users. Nouns in the interlingua correspond to 'object concepts' in the ontology, which also contains 'event concepts', such as the event **remove**, corresponding to the English verb *remove* and the Japanese verb *torinozoku* (by no means are all mappings from the interlingua into natural language as straightforward as this, for example, the concept **to-press-button** must be divided into subevents corresponding to pressing, holding down and releasing the button). Concepts are represented in a form of frame representation language, familiar from work in Artificial Intelligence and Natural Language Processing, in which frames (providing an intrinsic characterisation of concepts) are linked in a hierarchical network. To give an idea of the amount of detailed knowledge about concepts that one might want to encode, Table 10.1 gives by way of example a frame for the concept **computer**.

Knowledge-based MT is still pursued today at CMU in the KANT system, but is much more modest in terms of its goals for domain knowledge, which is limited to that which is necessary for stylistically adequate, accurate translation, as opposed to deep textual understanding. Thus the domain model simply represents all the concepts relevant in the domain, but does not support any further reasoning or inference about the concepts in the domain, other than that which is directly encoded (e.g. hierarchical information such as the fact that personal computers and mainframes are types of computer). The essential role of the domain model is to support full disambiguation of the text. An important part of this is specifying, for every event concept in the domain, what restrictions it places on the object concepts which constitute its arguments (e.g. only living things can die, only humans can think, in a literal sense) or the 'fillers' of 'slots' in its (frame-based) representation.

Once you start adding detailed knowledge in the pursuit of high quality transla-

Subclasses	personal-computer mini mainframe super
is-a	independent device
has-as-part	software computer-keyboard input-device disk-drive
	output-device CD-Rom card computer-hardware-card cpu
	memory-expansion-card monitor printer system unit
max-users	(<>1 200)
make	Plus AT XT 750 780
token	"The basic IBM Personal Computer consists of a system
	unit and keyboard"
Part-of	airport-check-in-facility security-check-device
operational	yes no
manufactured-by	intentional-agent
configuration	minimal regular extra
theme-of	device-event spatial-event

Table 10.1 Example Frame for the concept `computer`

tion through text understanding, it is tempting to add more and more sources of knowledge. It is quite clear that anaphora resolution and the resolution of other referential ambiguities requires reference to a level of structure above sentential syntax and semantics (see e.g. the examples in Chapter 6). Likewise, for stylistic reasons, to increase the cohesiveness of the text, one might need to keep some working representation of the paragraph structure. Achieving a really high quality translation, especially with some sorts of text, might require treatment of metaphor, metonymy, indirect speech acts, speaker/hearer attitudes and so on. Over the last few years a variety of groups in different parts of the world have begun experimenting with prototypes intended to work with explicit knowledge or rule components dealing with a wide variety of different types of information. All of these approaches can be viewed as examples, of one form or another, of knowledge-based MT.

10.2.3 Feasibility of General Purpose Rule-Based MT Systems

The approaches to MT that we have discussed so far in this chapter can be distinguished from each other mainly in terms of the various knowledge sources which are used in translation. They are all straightforward rule-based approaches, as most work in MT has been until the last few years. However it is widely recognised that there are serious challenges in building a robust, general purpose, high quality rule-based MT system, given the current state of linguistic knowledge. As we shall see, these problems and the increasing availability of raw materials in the form of on-line dictionaries, termbanks and corpus resources have led to a number of new developments in recent years which rely on empirical methods of various sorts, seeking to minimize or at least make more tractable the linguistic knowledge engineering problem.

One of the most serious problems, and probably *the* most serious problem, for linguistic knowledge MT is the development of appropriate large-scale grammatical and lexical resources. There are really a number of closely related problems here. The first is simply the scale of the undertaking, in terms of numbers of linguistic rules and lexical entries needed for fully automatic, high quality MT for general purpose and specialised language usage. Even assuming that our current state of linguistic knowledge is sophisticated enough, the effort involved is awesome, if all such information must be manually coded. It is generally accepted, then, that techniques must be adopted which favour the introduction of semi-automatic and automatic acquisition of linguistic knowledge.

The second concerns the difficulties of manipulating and managing such knowledge within a working system. The experience of linguists developing a wide variety of natural language processing systems shows that it is all too easy to add ad hoc, specially crafted rules to deal with problem cases, with the result that the system soon becomes difficult to understand, upgrade and maintain. In the worst case, the addition of a new rule to bring about some intended improvement, may cause the entire edifice to topple and performance to degrade. To a certain extent, these familiar problems can be avoided by adopting up to date formalisms, and restricting the use of special devices as much as possible. It is also very important to do everything possible to ensure that different grammar writers adopt essentially the same or consistent approaches and document everything they do in detail.

The third issue is one of quality and concerns the level of linguistic detail required to make the various discriminations which are necessary to ensure high quality output, at least for general texts. This problem shows up in a number of different areas, most notably in discriminating between different senses of a word, but also in relating pronouns to their antecedents.

Some consider that this third aspect is so serious as to effectively undermine the possibility of building large scale robust general purpose MT systems with a reasonably high quality output, arguing that given the current state of our understanding of (especially) sense differences, we are at the limits of what is possible for the time being in terms of the explicit encoding of linguistic distinctions. An extremely radical approach to this problem is to try to do away with explicitly formulated linguistic knowledge completely. This extreme form of the 'empirical' approach to MT is found in the work carried out by an MT group at IBM Yorktown Heights and will be discussed in the section below on Statistical Approaches.

One interesting development is now evident which receives its impetus from the appreciation of the difficulty and costliness of linguistic knowledge engineering. This is the growth of research into the reusability of resources (from application to application and from project to project) and the eventual development of standards for common resources. One of the reasons why this is happening now is that there is undoubtedly a set of core techniques and approaches which are widely known and accepted within the Natural Language Processing research community. In this sense a partial consensus is emerging on the treatment of some linguistic phenomena. A second important motivation is a growing appreciation of the fact that sharing tools, techniques and the grammatical and lexical resources between projects, for the areas where there is a consensus, allows one to direct research more appropriately at those issues which pose challenges.

As well as the various difficulties in developing linguistic resources, there are other issues which must be addressed in the development of a working MT system. If a system is to be used on free text, then it must be robust. That is, it must have mechanisms for dealing with unknown words and ill-formed output (simply answering 'no' and refusing to proceed would not be cooperative behaviour). In a similar way, it must have a way of dealing with unresolved ambiguities, that is, cases in which the grammar rules, in the light of all available information, still permit a number of different analyses. This is likely to happen in terms of both lexical choice (for example, where there are a number of alternatives for a given word in translation) and structural choice. For example, taken in isolation (and in all likelihood, even in many contexts) the following string is ambiguous as shown:

(6)   a.   Sam told Kim that Jo had died last week.

    b.   Sam told Kim [that Jo had died] last week.

    c.   Sam told Kim [that Jo had died last week].

Such attachment ambiguities with adverbial phrases (such as *last week*) and prepositional phrases (*on Tuesday*) occur quite frequently in a language like English in which PPs and ADVPs typically occur at the end of phrases. In many cases, they are strictly structurally ambiguous, but can be disambiguated in context by the hearer by using real-word knowledge. For example, the following *is* ambiguous, but the hearer of such a sentence would have enough shared knowledge with the speaker to chose the intended interpretation (and perhaps would not even be aware of the ambiguity):

(7)   a.   Joe bought the book that I had been trying to obtain for Susan.

    b.   [Joe bought [the book that I had been trying to obtain for Susan]].

    c.   [Joe bought [the book that I had been trying to obtain] for Susan].

Consideration of issues such as these underlies work in integrating core MT engines with spelling checkers, fail-safe routines for what to do when a word in the input is not in the dictionary and adding preference mechanisms which chose an analysis in cases of true ambiguity, but an appreciation of the serious nature of these issues has also provided an motivation for the current interest in empirical, corpus or statistical-based MT, to which we return after discussing the question of resources for MT.

10.3 Resources for MT

As researchers begin to consider the implications of developing their systems beyond the level of proof-of-concept research prototypes with very restricted coverage, considerable attention is being paid to the role that existing bilingual and monolingual corpus and lexical resources can play. A corpus is essentially a large collection of texts, but for our purposes we are interested only in such texts stored on computers in a standard format (e.g. extended ASCII). Such texts may often contain standard markup (e.g. in SGML) and for most practical purposes one needs a set of corpus access tools for retrieving data at will.

Various research centres throughout the world have been developing monolingual corpus resources for many years, and there has been a growing awareness throughout the eighties of their importance to linguistic and lexicographic work. A number of sites hold substantial corpus resources (several millions of words), an example being the Unit for Computer Research on the English Language at the University of Lancaster which currently holds in excess of 5 million words of corpus material, of which 4M words have been tagged with part-of-speech information. Such collections are a rich repository of information about actual language usage. Efforts are underway at different centres to (automatically or semi-automatically) annotate corpus resources with various types of linguistic information, in addition to grammatical (POS) tagging, prosodic annotation (indicating features of stress and annotation), syntactic tagging (indicating phrasal groups of words, i.e. parsing or partial (skeleton) parsing); semantic tagging and discourse level tagging (indicating anaphoric and other similar links). To give some idea of scale, the planned British National Corpus will contain around 100M words of grammatically tagged corpus material, with standard SGML markup. The following example text has been tagged with the CLAWS tagset developed at UCREL, University of Lancaster — in cases where multiple tags are possible, the tag chosen by the probabilistic tagger is shown in square brackets, with the alternatives following after commas.

These tags, which it must be stressed are assigned completely automatically and with a high level of accuracy, provide a detailed parts of speech analysis of the text, distinguishing between some 40 different subcategories of Noun (the tags for Nouns begin with N for Noun or P for pronoun) and some 30 different subcategories of Verb, and so on.

Over the last few years there has been an increasing awareness of the importance of corpus resources in MT research. Tools for extracting information automatically from texts are being increasingly used, and new techniques developed. At the simplest level, a monolingual corpus is a crucial tool for the linguist in determining language usage in a given domain, and a bilingual corpus for determining the facts of translation. In developing MT systems, bilingual texts are an extremely important resource, and they are most useful if organized in such a way that the user can view translation 'chunks' or 'units'. In **bitext** (or 'multitext') the text is aligned so that within each bilingual (or multilingual) chunk the texts are translations of each other.

Excerpt from a Tagged Corpus

Satellite_[JJ], NN1 communications_NN2 have_VH0 been_VBN used_[VVN], VVD, JJ for_[IF], CF, RP almost_RR two_MC decades_NNT2 to_TO provide_VVI intercontinental_[JJ], NN1 traffic_[NN1], VV0 through_[II], RP, JB the_AT INTELSAT_[NNJ], VV0, NN1 ,_, INTERSPUTNIK_[NN1], NNJ and_CC INMARSAT_[VV0], NN1,NNJ systems_NN2 ._. INTELSAT_VVC, now_[RT], CS also_RR provides_VVZ regional_JJ traffic_[NN1], VV and_CC leases_[NN2], VVZ transponders_[VVZ], NN2 to_[II], TO, RP several_DA2 countries_NNL2 for_[IF], CF, RP domestic_[JJ], NN1 use_[NN1], VV0 ._.

The most common form of alignment takes the sentence to be the organizing unit for chunking and techniques exist for performing this alignment of bitext automatically with a high level of accuracy (96% or higher). Of course alignment does not need to stop at the sentence level and it is possible to apply simple probability measures to a sentence aligned bitext to extract automatically the most probable word pair alignments, and given some skeleton or phrasal parsing, to attempt to extract useful information about phrasal alignment. A caveat is of course in order — the success of techniques such as probabilistic word pair alignment depends on the size and quality of the corpus resource, and minimum size is probably 2M words of clean text. The availability of bilingual or multilingual corpus resources of a decent size is currently a limiting factor. Despite the fact that many international institutions and companies have large bilingual or multilingual resources in appropriate formats, they have been slow to appreciate the value of releasing these to the research community, although there are indications that this situation is now changing (the Canadian English-French Hansard record of parliamentary proceedings is a notable exception, see the extract on page 197).

Much of the interest in corpus resources and machine-readable dictionaries comes not from their value as static knowledge banks, which the grammar writer can consult but in the possibilities of using the information they contain directly in the MT system, thus providing some solution to the knowledge acquisition problem we noted above. One way this can be achieved is by investigating procedures for automatically or semi-automatically deriving linguistic rules for the MT system from the various sources of information. Ideas currently under investigation include the use of monolingual corpus of sufficient size for automatic sense disambiguation in context.[2] As a further example, a part of speech tagged sentence aligned bilingual

---

[2]This may use the measure of Mutual Information, taking into account (roughly) the amount of mutual context elements share

Extract from Bilingual Hansard

French

Score 24 Que la Chambre blâme le gouvernement pour son inaction dans les dossiers de la grande région de Montréal, comprenant l' Agence spatiale, le développement du Vieux-Port, l' aménagement du Port, le projet Soligaz, les chantiers maritimes , la relance économique de l' est de Montréal, ainsi que la détérioration de l' économie du sud-ouest de la région.

Score 52 Monsieur le Président, je pense qu' il est important de rappeler pourquoi aujourd'hui, nous, du parti libéral, déposons une telle motion de blâme à l' endroit de ce gouvernement, après trois ans et demi de pouvoir, concernant les dossiers de Montréal, principal centre du Québec et aussi du Canada, un des principaux centres.

Score 8 Pourquoi il y a tant de dossiers pour qu' aujourd'hui on en arrive à une motion de blâme à l' endroit du gouvernement?

Score 86 Il est tout simplement important de se rappeler qu' après les élections de 1984, et suite à de multiple promesses faites par ce gouvernement à la population montréalaise, aux autorités municipales, aux gens de tout le Québec, dès 1985, malgré une représentation de 56 ou 57 députés, huit députés conservateurs sur l' île de Montréal, le milieu des affaires commence à se plaindre.

English

Score 24 That this House condemns the government for its failure to act in matters of interest to the region of Greater Montreal, including the space agency, the development of the Vieux-Port, the planning and development of Montreal Harbour, the Soligaz project, the shipyards and the economic renewal of East Montreal as well as the economic deterioration of the southwestern part of the region.

Score 52 He said : Mr. Speaker, I think it is important to recall why today, we in the Liberal Party move this motion to condemn a Government that has been in power for three and half years, a motion that concerns matters of interest to Montreal, the main urban centre of Quebec and one of the major urban centres in this country.

Score 8 Why has the number of issues outstanding increased to the point that today, we moved a motion condemning the Government?

Score 86 We must remember that after the election in 1984, following the many promises made by this Government to the people of Montreal, the municipal authorities and Quebecers as a whole, that in 1985, despite strong representation consisting of fifty-six or fifty-seven Members, including eight Conservative Members on Montreal Island, the business community started to complain.

text together with some probabilistic model, could be used to automatically provide equivalent terms in the two languages which could then be automatically compiled into the relevant formalism for lexical entries in an MT system.

A further resource which is now beginning to be adequately exploited is the machine-readable dictionary (cf. Chapter 5). Monolingual lexical entries can be constructed semi-automatically from machine-readable dictionaries, and research is underway into semi-automatically deriving a bilingual lexicon from these monolingual lexica by statistical comparison of the lexical structures associated with various word senses. Another possibility is that of automatically deriving subcategorization and semantic selectional information for lexical entries and grammatical rules from corpus resources and machine-readable dictionaries. In all of these applications, the knowledge banks can be used to ease the formulation of large amounts of detailed linguistic information in a rule-based system. A number of other approaches, to which we now turn, attempt to use the information implicit in bilingual corpora, dictionaries and thesauri much more directly, as a component in the MT system.

10.4   Empirical Approaches to MT

Given the questions that have been raised about the feasibility of 'rule-based' approaches, the increasing availability of large amounts of machine readable textual material has been seen by a number of research groups as opening possibilities for rather different MT architectures — in particular, so called 'empirical' architectures which apply relatively 'low-level' statistical or pattern matching techniques either directly to texts, or to texts that have been subject to only rather superficial analysis. The reasoning behind the term empirical is that in such approaches, whatever linguistic knowledge the system uses is derived empirically, by examination of real texts, rather than being reasoned out by linguists. We will look at two such approaches: the so called 'example' or 'analogy' based approach, and the 'statistical' approach.

10.4.1   Example-Based Translation

Throughout most of this book, we have assumed a model of the translation machine which involves explicit mapping rules of various sorts. In the 'translation by analogy', or 'example-based' approach, such mapping rules are dispensed with in favour of a procedure which involves matching against stored example translations. The basic idea is to collect a bilingual corpus of translation pairs and then use a best match algorithm to find the closest example to the source phrase in question. This gives a translation template, which can then be filled in by word-for-word translation.

This idea is sometimes thought to be reminiscent of how human translators proceed when using a bilingual dictionary: looking at the examples given to find the source language example that best approximates what they are trying to translate, and constructing a translation on the basis of the target language example that is given. For example, the bilingual dictionary entry for *printer* which we discussed in Chapter 5 gave the following as examples.

(8) a. ∼'s **error** faute *f* d'impression, coquille *f*;

  b. ∼'s **reader** correcteur *m*, -trice *f* (d'épreuves).

Given a sentence like (8) to translate, a human translator would certainly choose *faute d'impression* or *coquille* as the translation, on the basis that a mistake is much more like an error than it is like a reader.

(9) This seems to be ⎡a printer's mistake⎤.

The distance calculation, to find the best match for the source phrase, can involve calculating the closeness of items in a hierarchy of terms and concepts provided by a thesaurus. To give a flavour of the idea, and the sort of problem it addresses, consider the problem of translating Japanese phrases of the form *A no B* (*no* is a particle indicating the relation between A and B) into English. Among the forms to choose from are *AB*, *A's B*, *B of A*, *B on A*, *B in A*, and *B for A*, cf Table 10.2 which gives English paraphrases of examples involving *no*, together with the correct translations for these different patterns. The problem is certainly not an esoteric one, since the expression is claimed to occur in around 50% of Japanese sentences.

B of A	8th *no* afternoon	the afternoon of the 8th
B for A	conference *no* application fee	the application fee for the conference
B in A	Kyoto *no* conference	the conference in Kyoto
A's B	a week *no* holiday	a week's holiday
AB	hotel *no* reservation	the hotel reservation
AB	three *no* hotel	three hotels

Table 10.2 Alternative Translations for the Particle *no*

For a given input, the system will then calculate how close it is to various stored example translations based on the distance of the input from the example in terms of the thesaurus hierarchy (this involves finding the 'Most Specific Common Abstraction' for the input and the alternative translations — i.e. 'closest' concept in the thesaurus hierarchy) and how 'likely' the various translations are on the basis of frequency ratings for elements in the database of examples. (Notice this means we assume that the database of examples is representative of the texts we intend to translate.)

The following is an extension to this basic idea: pairs of equivalent source and target language expression are given, along with example translations, written in parentheses, and interpreted as stating 'conditions' under which the given equivalence holds. For example, the rule for the Japanese word *sochira* ('this', or 'this person' — i.e. the addressee, *you*), given below, indicates that *sochira* translates as *this* when the example involves *desu*, (translating as *be*), and as *you*, when the input involves something like *okuru* (translating as *send*). In translating an input like *sochira ni tsutaeru*, the English pronoun *you* would be selected as the translation of *sochira*, because *tsutaeru* (convey) is closest to *okuru* (send) in the thesaurus.

```
sochira
→
this (( desu {be}),...)
you (( okuru {send}),...)
this (( miru {see}),...)
```

This rule uses only information about the surrounding string, but one could imagine other sorts of example, where information is given in terms of patterns of strings, or of grammatical information. An example involving string patterns is given below, which would be involved in translating examples involving the expression *o-negaishimasu* along the lines of (9) (*o-negaishimasu* ('please') is a general expression indicating that a request is being made, or a favour requested, *o* indicates that the preceding noun phrase is an OBJECT).

(10) a. jinjika o o-negaishimasu.
          personnel section OBJ please
          May I speak to the personnel section?

      b. daimei o o-negaishimasu.
          title OBJ please
          Please give me the title.

To deal with this, rules like the following use information about surrounding string *patterns*:

```
X o o-negaishimasu
→
May I speak to X' ((jimukyoku {office}),...)
Please give me X' ((bangou {number}),...)
```

It should be evident that the feasibility of the approach depends crucially on the collection of good data. However, one of the advantages of the approach is that the quality of translation will improve incrementally as the example set becomes more complete, without the need to update and improve detailed grammatical and lexical descriptions. Moreover, the approach can be (in principle) very efficient, since in the best case there is no complex rule application to perform — all one has to do is find the appropriate example and (sometimes) calculate distances. However, there are some complications. For example, one problem arises when one has a number of different examples each of which matches part of the string, but where the parts they match overlap, and/or do not cover the whole string. In such cases, calculating the best match can involve considering a large number of possibilities.

A pure example-based approach would use no grammar rules at all, only example phrases. However, one could also imagine a role for some normal linguistic analysis, producing a standard linguistic representation. If, instead of being given in simple 'string' form, examples were stated in terms of such representations (i.e. given as fragments of linguistic representations), one would expect to be able to deal with many more variations in sentence pattern, and allow for a certain amount of restructuring in generation. In this way, one would have something that looked more like a standard LK architecture. The chief difference would be in the level of specificity of the rules. In particular, where in a traditional transfer system the rules are stated in as general a form as possible, to cover entire classes of case, what one would have here is a system where the rules are stated in highly particular forms (each one for essentially one case), but there is a general procedure for estimating, for each case, which rule is most appropriate (i.e. by estimating which example is closest). Of course, what this suggests is that there is no radical incompatibility between example-based, and rule-based approaches, so that the real challenge lies in finding the best combination of techniques from each. Here one obvious possibility is to use traditional rule-based transfer as a fall back, to be used only if there is no complete example-based translation.

10.4.2 Statistical MT

Over the last few years there has been a growing interest in the research community in statistical approaches to Natural Language Processing. With respect to MT, the term 'statistical approaches' can be understood in a narrow sense to refer to approaches which try to do away with explicitly formulating linguistic knowledge, or in a broad sense to denote the application of statistically or probablistically based techniques to parts of the MT task (e.g. as a word sense disambiguation component). We will give a flavour of this work by describing a pure statistical-based approach to MT.

The approach can be thought of as trying to apply to MT techniques which have been highly successful in Speech Recognition, and though the details require a reasonable amount of statistical sophistication, the basic idea can be grasped quite simply. The two key notions involved are those of the **language model** and the **translation model**. The language model provides us with probabilities for strings of words (in fact sentences), which we can denote by $\Pr(S)$ (for a source sentence S) and $\Pr(T)$ (for any given target sentence T). Intuitively, $\Pr(S)$ is the probability of a string of source words S occurring, and likewise for $\Pr(T)$. The translation model also provides us with probabilities — $\Pr(T|S)$ is the conditional probability that a target sentence T will occur in a target text which translates a text containing the source sentence S. The product of this and the probability of S itself, that is $Pr(S) \times Pr(T|S)$ gives the the probability of source-target pairs of sentences occurring, written $Pr(S,T)$.

One task, then, is to find out the probability of a source string (or sentence) occurring (i.e. $Pr(S)$). This can be decomposed into the probability of the first word, multiplied by the conditional probabilities of the succeeding words, as follows.

$$Pr(s1) \times Pr(s2|s1) \times Pr(s3|s1,s2), \text{ etc...}$$

Intuitively, the conditional probability $Pr(s2|s1)$ is the probability that s2 will occur, given that s1 has occurred; for example, the probability that *am* and *are* occur in a text might be approximately the same, but the probability of *am* occurring after *I* is quite high, while that of *are* is much lower). To keep things within manageable limits, it is common practice to take into account only the preceding one or two words in calculating these conditional probabilities (these are known respectively as 'bigram' and 'trigram' models). In order to calculate these source language probabilities (producing the source language model by estimating the parameters), a large amount of monolingual data is required, since of course the validity, usefulness or accuracy of the model will depend mainly on the size of the corpus.

The second task requiring large amounts of data is specifying the parameters of the translation model, which requires a large bilingual aligned corpus. As we observed above, there are rather few such resources, however, the research group at IBM which has been mainly responsible for developing this approach had access to three million sentence pairs from the Canadian (French-English) Hansard — the official record of proceedings in the Canadian Parliament (cf. the extract given above), from which they have developed a (sentence-) aligned corpus, where each source sentence is paired with its translation in the target language, as can be seen on page 203.

It is worth noting in passing that the usefulness of corpus resources depends very much on the state in which they are available to the researcher. Corpus clean-up and especially the correction of errors is a time-consuming and expensive business, and some would argue that it detracts from the 'purity' of the data. But the extract given here illustrates a potential source of problems if a corpus is not cleaned up in some ways — the penultimate French sentence contains a false start, followed by ..., while the English text (presumably produced by a human translator) contains just a complete sentence. This sort of divergence could in principle effect the statistics for word-level alignment.

In order to get some idea of how the translation model works, it is useful to introduce some further notions. In a word-aligned sentence-pair, it is indicated which target words correspond to each source word. An example of this (which takes French as the source language) is given in the second extract.

A Sentence-Aligned Corpus

Often, in the textile industry, businesses close their plant in Montreal to move to the Eastern Townships.
Dans le domaine du textile souvent, dans Montréal, on ferme et on va s' installer dans les Cantons de l' Est.

There is no legislation to prevent them from doing so, for it is a matter of internal economy.
Il n' y a aucune loi pour empêcher cela, c' est de la régie interne.

But then, in the case of the Gulf refinery it is different : first of all, the Federal Government asked Petro-Canada to buy everything, except in Quebec.
Mais là, la différence entre la Gulf... c' est différent parce que la vente de la raffinerie Gulf: premièrement, le gouvernement fédéral a demandé à Petro-Canada de tout acheter, sauf le Québec.

That is serious.
C'est grave.

Word Aligned Corpus

The Federal Government asked Petro-Canada to buy everything.
Le(1) gouvernement(3) fédéral(2) a demandé(4) à Petro-Canada(5) de(6) tout(8) acheter(7).

The numbers after the source words indicate the string position of the corresponding target word or words. If there is no target correspondence, then no bracketted numbers appear after the source word (e.g. *a* in *a demandé*). If more than one word in the target corresponds, then this is also indicated. The **fertility** of a source word is the number of words corresponding to it in the target string. For example, the fertility of *asked* with English as source language is 2, since it aligns with *a demandé*. A third notion is that of **distortion** which refers to the fact that source words and their target correspondences do not necessarily appear in the same string position (compare *tout acheter* and *buy everything*, for example).

The parameters which must be calculated from the bilingual sentence aligned corpus are then (i) the fertility probabilities for each source word (i.e. the likelihood of it translating as one, two, three, etc, words respectively), (ii) the word-pair or translation possibilities for each word in each language and (iii) the set of distortion probabilities for each source and target position. With this information (which is extracted automatically from the corpus), the translation model can, for a given S, calculate $Pr(T|S)$ (that is, the probability of T, given S). This is the essence of the approach to statistically-based MT, although the procedure is itself slightly more complicated in involving search through possible source language sentences for the one which maximises $Pr(S) \times Pr(T|S)$, translation being essentially viewed as the problem of finding the S that is most probable given T — i.e. one wants to maximise $Pr(S|T)$. Given that

$$Pr(S|T) = \frac{Pr(S)Pr(T|S)}{Pr(T)}$$

then one just needs to choose S that maximizes the product of $Pr(S)$ and $Pr(T|S)$.

It should be clear that in an approach such as this there is no role whatsoever for the explicit encoding of linguistic information, and thus the knowledge acquisition problem is solved. On the other hand, the general applicability of the method might be doubted, since as we observed above, it is heavily dependent on the availability of good quality bilingual or multilingual data in very large proportions, something which is currently lacking for most languages.

Results to date in terms of accuracy have not been overly impressive, with a 39% rate of correct translation reported on a set of 100 short test sentences. A defect of this approach is that morphologically related words are treated as completely separate from each other, so that, for example, distributional information about *sees* cannot contribute to the calculation of parameters for *see* and *saw*, etc. In an attempt to remedy this defect, researchers at IBM have started to add low level grammatical information piecemeal to their system, moving in essence towards an analysis-transfer-synthesis model of statistically-based translation. The information in question includes morphological information, the neutralisation of case distinctions (upper and lower case) and minor transformations to input sentences (such as the movement of adverbs) to create a more canonical form. The currently reported success rate with 100 test sentences is a quite respectable 60%. A major criticism of this move is of course precisely that linguistic information is being added piecemeal, without a real view of its appropriacy or completeness, and there must be serious doubts about how far the approach can be extended without further additions of explicit linguistic knowledge, i.e. a more systematic notion of grammar. Putting the matter more positively, it seems clear that there is a useful role for information about probabilities. However, the poor success rate for the 'pure' approach without any linguistic knowledge (less than 40%) suggests that the real question is how one can best combine statistical and rule-based approaches.

10.5   Summary

We have tried in this chapter to give a brief overview of some of the issues and techniques which are being actively researched today in MT. Of course, there is not enough room in one chapter to do justice to the field, and we have of necessity omitted much work that is of interest. In particular, we have restricted our discussion to MT itself and have said nothing at all about recent work in the development of translators aids, multilingual authoring packages and terminological systems of various sorts. Nonetheless we have identified three important trends in current research in MT. The first is the exploitation of current techniques from computational linguistics to permit a multidimensional view of the translational relation between two texts. The second in the increasing orientation of the research community towards the use of existing resources of various sorts, either to extract useful information or directly as components in systems. The third, related, trend is towards statistical or empirical models of translation. Though we have dwelt in some detail in this short survey on 'pure' statistical and simple pattern matching methods, in fact much recent work advocates a mixture of techniques, for example with statistical methods supplementing rule-based methods in various ways.

10.6   Further Reading

Our discussion of flexible translation between Swedish and Norwegian is based on unpublished work by [Dyvik, 1992]. The standard references on sign-based approaches to linguistic representation are [Pollard and Sag, 1987; Pollard and Sag, 1993]. The view of constraint based translation that we describe is loosely modelled on that used in 'Shake and Bake' [Whitelock, 1992; Beaven, 1992]. See [Kaplan *et al.*, 1989], [Sadler, 1991] and [Sadler, 1993] for a slightly different approach. General discussion of how multi-dimensional representations can be used in MT can be found in [Sadler and Arnold, 1993].

On knowledge-based MT see [Goodman and Nirenburg, 1991], and the special issue of the journal *Machine Translation*, [Goodman, 1989].

On the processing of corpora, and their use in linguistics generally, see [Garside *et al.*, 1987], and [Aijmer and Altenberg, 1991].

The idea of example-based MT was first discussed in a paper by Nagao [Nagao, 1984]. For a review of more recent work along these lines, see [Somers, 1992].

The pure statistical approach to MT is based on the work of a team at IBM, see for example [Brown *et al.*, 1990]. As regards aligned, bilingual corpora, the most common form of alignment takes the sentence to be the organizing unit for chunking, see [Brown *et al.*, 1991] and [Gale and Church, 1991b] for relevant discussion. On automatic extraction of word correspondences across bitext, see [Gale and Church, 1991a]. Techniques involving the use of corpus resources for automatic sense disambiguation have also been explored within the DLT project, see [Sadler, 1989].

The translation of *no*, which was described around page 198 above, is discussed by [Sumita *et al.*, 1990]. The discussion of *o-negaishimasu* is from [Furuse and Iida, 1992b], see also [Furuse and Iida, 1992a], and [Sumita and Iida, 1991].

The frame for `computer` on page 192 above is taken from [Goodman and Nirenburg, 1991, page 25].

For up to date reports on research in the field of MT, there are several journals, and several major international conferences. The specialist Journal is *Machine Translation*, edited by Sergei Nirenburg, from Carnegie Mellon University in Pittsburg, USA, and published by Kluwer Academic Publishers. However, the journal *Computational Linguistics*, published by the MIT Press for the Association for Computational Linguistics (ACL), also publishes research which is directly about MT.

The specialist conference for research on MT is called *TMI* — for 'Theoretical and Methodological Issues (in Machine Translation)'. This has been held every two years since 1986, and proceedings are published ([TMI1, 1985],[TMI2, 1988][TMI3, 1990],[TMI4, 1992]). Many of the papers in the last of these are directly or indirectly about the issue of 'rationalist' (i.e. rule-based) vs. empirical approaches to MT. The proceedings of the main Computational Linguistics conferences, namely (*COLING*), the conferences of the Association for Computational Linguistics (ACL) and the conferences of the European Chapters of the ACL, also contain a high percentage of papers about MT. ACL conferences are held annually in the USA (for example, [ACL28, 1990; ACL29, 1991; ACL30, 1992]). The EACL conferences are held biennially, [EACL1, 1983; EACL2, 1985; EACL3, 1987; EACL4, 1989; EACL5, 1991], as is COLING: *Coling 84* [Coling84, 1984] was held in Stanford, California, *COLING 86* [Coling86, 1986] in Bonn, *Coling 88* [Coling88, 1988]in Budapest, *Coling 90* [Coling90, 1990] in Helsinki, and *Coling 92* [Coling92, 1992] was held in Nantes.

Useful Addresses

ASLIB,
The Association for Information Management,
Information House,
20-24, Old Street,
London, EC1V 9AP,
UK.

The Association for Computational Linguistics (ACL),
c/o Donald E. Walker,
Bellcore, MRE 2A379,
445 South Street, Box 1910,
Morristown, NJ 07960-1910,
USA.

The Association for Computational Linguistics (European Chapter),
c/o Michael Rosner,
IDSIA,
Corso Elvezia 36,
CH-6900 Lugano,
Switzerland.

Computational Linguistics,
MIT Press Journals,
55 Hayward Street,
Cambridge, MA 02142,
USA.

Language Industry Monitor,
Uitgeverij LIM,
Eerste Helmersstraat 183,
1054 DT Amsterdam,
The Netherlands.

Machine Translation,
Kluwer Academic Publishers,
PO Box 322,
3300 AH, Dordrecht,
The Netherlands.

American Association for Machine Translation,
Suite 310, 655, Fifteenth Street,
Washington, DC 20005,
USA.

Asia-Pacific Association for Machine Translation,
305 Akasaka Chuo Mansion, 2-17 Akasaka 7-chome,
Minato-ku, Tokyo 107,
Japan.

European Association for Machine Translation,
ISSCO,
54 route des Acacias,
CH-1227 Carouge (Geneva),
Switzerland.

International Association for Machine Translation,
c/o AMTA,
Suite 310, 655, Fifteenth Street, NW,
Washington, DC 20005,
USA.

Glossary

adjective phrase (AP) a complete construction **headed** by an adjective. APs typically modify nouns and occur as complements to verbs such as *be, seem, become.* For example: *The man* **guilty of this heinous crime** *was imprisoned. John seems rather stupid.*

adjunct or modifier an optional or secondary element in a construction which can be removed without affecting the structural status of the rest of the construction. For example, *yesterday* in: *John kicked the ball yesterday* (Compare *John kicked the ball* where *the ball* is not an adjunct, because **John kicked yesterday* is ungrammatical).

affix morpheme placed at the beginning (prefix), middle (infix), or end (**suffix**) of the **root** or **stem** of a word, e.g. re*legal*ize.

agreement the process whereby the form of one word requires a corresponding form of another - for example, the plural form *boys* requires a plural form of the demonstrative determiner *these/*this*: *these boys* vs **this boys.*

algorithm a prescribed set of well-defined rules or instructions for the solution of a problem.

analysis the phase in natural language processing systems (including MT systems) in which a structure or representation is assigned to source language (input) sentences or the representation itself or the name for the module of linguistic rules involved.

anaphor a word or phrase which refers back to some previously expressed word or phrase or meaning (typically, pronouns such as *herself, himself, he, she*).

antecedent the word or phrase to which a later word or phrase (e.g. an **anaphor**) refers.

Artificial Intelligence (AI) the branch of Computing Science concerned with simulating aspects of human intelligence such as language comprehension and production, vision, planning, etc.

ASCII American Standard Code for Information Interchange - a standard set of codes used for representing alphanumeric information in a computer.

aspect a property of verbs or sentences, which refers primarily to the duration or type of activity described, e.g. the distinction between *Sam sang* and *Sam was singing*.

attribute value pair Many contemporary linguistic analyses use collections of features or attribute value pairs to encode various properties of a linguistic entity. In the pair [number sing], *number* is the attribute and *sing* is the value.

auxiliary (AUX) in English, auxiliary verbs are those which carry distinctions of **tense**, **aspect**, etc, such as *do, be* and *have*. The **modal** auxiliaries include *can/could, may/might, shall/should, ought to, need* and *used to*. Auxiliary verbs are opposed to **main** verbs (*walk, play*, etc.)

batch (processing) as opposed to interactive processing. In batch processing, a computer does not perform tasks as soon as requested, but groups similar jobs together into batches and carries them out together at some later time (e.g. overnight). Interactive processing allows the user to issue an instruction and have it carried out more or less instantly.

bitext a bilingual text which is aligned so that within each bilingual chunk the texts are translations of each other. The use of the term does not necessarily commit one as to the level at which a text is chunked and aligned, e.g. into sentences or paragraphs, but the chunks are very often sentences.

case a property of words, primarily nouns, which varies according to their syntactic function. English distinguishes three cases of pronouns, one used for pronouns which are the subject of finite verbs (*he, I*) one for possessive pronouns (*his,my*) and one for pronouns elsewhere (*him, me*). The case system of many other languages is much more extensive.

CD-Rom a compact disc used for the storage of data in read-only (ROM) format.

collocation phrases composed of words that co-occur for lexical rather than semantic reasons, for example, a *heavy smoker* is one who smokes a great deal, but someone who writes a great deal is not a *heavy writer*. This seems to be a lexical fact, not related to the meanings of *smoker* or *writer*.

common sense reasoning reasoning on the basis of common knowledge, as opposed to purely logical reasoning, or reasoning that depends solely on the meanings of words. A purely logical inference might be from *If it is Tuesday, Sam is in London* and *It is Tuesday* to the conclusion *Sam is in London*. An example of common sense reasoning might be the inference that if someone asks for a phone book it is because they want to look up a number, and make a phone call.

complement a term for all constituents of the sentence required by a verb except for the subject (e.g. the object is a complement of the verb).

compound two or more words which function as one word (e.g. *fireplace, videotape, door handle*). Most common in English and closely related languages are noun-noun compounds functioning as nouns. Because such compounds have the external behaviour and distribution of a lexical item, they are often taken to be morphological structures.

constituent a linguistic unit which is a component of a larger construction. These units can, in turn, be analysed into further constituents (e.g. a **noun phrase** can be analysed into a determiner and a **noun**).

constituent structure the structure of an expression in terms of the **constituent** syntactic parts and their categories (as opposed to analysis in terms of grammatical or semantic relations).

context all the factors which systematically determine the form, meaning, appropriateness or translation of linguistic expressions. One can distinguish between linguistic context (provided by the preceding utterances or text) and non-linguistic context (including shared assumptions and information).

controlled language a specially simplified version of a language which is adopted (typically by a company or a documentation section of a company) as a partial solution to a perceived communication problem. Both the vocabulary and the syntactic structures may be restricted.

corpus collection of linguistic data, either written texts or a transcription of recorded speech. Typically, corpora have to be quite large to be of any linguistic use (upwards of 100,000 tokens).

critiquing system a computer program which analyses a text and indicates where it deviates from the norms of language use.

database generally, any collection of information that can be created, accessed, and processed automatically. Many sophisticated software packages exist for creating and accessing databases of information.

dependency grammar a type of grammar which operates essentially in terms of types of dependencies or grammatical relation between heads and dependent elements of a construction rather than in terms of constituent structure.

derivational a term used in **morphology** to refer to one of the two main processes of work-formation, the other being **inflectional**. Derivational processes result in words of a different class. In English, the major derivational process is suffixation, e.g. *derive - derivation, happy - happiness, nation - national.*

electronic dictionary dictionary which is stored on computer and can be accessed by programs, e.g. so that definitions can be looked up and displayed on screen.

feature see **attribute-value pair**

finite a form of a **verb** that can occur as the head of a sentence. In *Sam wants to leave, wants* is finite, *leave* is non-finite.

gender 2 types of gender are distinguished in linguistics — natural gender, where items refer to the sex of real world entities, and grammatical gender, which has nothing to do with sex, but which signals grammatical relationships between words in a sentence and which is shown e.g. by the form of the article or the noun.

generation (also synthesis) the phase in a natural language processing system (including MT systems) in which a strings or sentences are produced from some sort of underlying representation, typically a meaning representation of some sort or the name for the module of linguistic rules which causes this to happen.

grammar the term is generally used to include **syntax** and **morphology** but may also be used in a wider sense to include rules of **phonology** and **semantics**. A grammar is a collection of linguistic rules which define a language.

grammatical relations the relations which hold between a **head** (such as a verb) and its **dependents**. For example, subject and object are grammatical relations borne by constituents in a sentence.

head the central or most important element in a construction which determines the external distribution of the construction and places certain requirements on the words or constituents it occurs with. For example, the verb *saw* is head of the sentence *The big man saw Mary* and of the VP *saw Mary*. Nouns are heads of NPs, prepositions are heads of PPs, adjectives of APs, etc. In lexicography, head is another term for **headword**.

headword word forming the heading of an entry in a dictionary.

homographs words which have the same spelling but which differ in meaning, e.g. *bank* (financial institution) and *bank* (of a river).

idiom a sequence of words which functions semantically as a unit and with an unpredictable meaning (e.g. *kick the bucket*, meaning *die*). This is generally accompanied by a degree of syntactic restriction.

imperative verb forms or sentence types that are used to express commands (e.g. *Go away!*)

indexical a word which depends on the context of utterance for its meaning (e.g. *I, you, here*).

indirect object (IOBJ) the constituent of a sentence most typically associated with the goal or recipient role. In English indirect objects are often PPs with the preposition *to*, e.g. *Lee gave the book* **to his friend.**

inflectional term in **morphology** assigned to affixes which encode grammatical properties such as **number, tense** and do not change the **part of speech** of the **stems** to which they are attached.

interlingual language independent, a linguistic knowledge based approach to MT where translation proceeds in 2 stages - **analysis** (where input string is mapped onto a language independence representation) and **generation**, cf. transfer.

intransitive a verb that does not take a **direct object** (e.g. *die*).

lexicon used synonymously with dictionary.

light verbs (also **support verbs**) verbs that are semantically empty or relatively empty (e.g. *take* in *take a walk*).

markup codes in some (text formatting) description language which determine how text will look when printed.

metaphor in metaphorical usage, expressions are used in a way that appears literally false. For example, using the word *boiling* to describe water which is simply too hot for comfort.

mood a term applied to **sentences** and **verbs** to signal a wide range of meanings, especially speaker's attitude to the factual content of utterances, e.g. certainty, possibility (e.g. *Sam must/may be at home*). The distinction between active and passive sentences/verbs is also sometimes considered a mood.

morphology the branch of **grammar** which studies the structure or forms of words. The main branches are **inflectional morphology, derivational morphology,** and **compounding.**

natural language a term which denotes a (naturally occurring) human language as opposed to computer languages and other artificial languages.

NLP (Natural Language Processing) the field of inquiry concerned with the study and development of computer systems for processing natural (human) languages.

noun phrase (NP) a complete construction **headed** by a **noun**. It can be substituted by, or act as antecedent for, a pronoun of the appropriate sort:
[*NP The man who I saw yesterday*] *has just knocked at the door. Can you let* **him** *in?*

number the number of a noun or noun phrase generally corresponds to the number of real world entities referred to (e.g. singular NPs denote single individuals (*a table*), plural NPs denote collections of individuals (*two tables*). However the relationship between real number and grammatical number is not always straightforward - *trousers* is plural in form yet denotes a singular entity (as in *the committee are considering that question this afternoon*) and some nouns do not have distinct singular and plural forms (*sheep, salmon*).

object (OBJ) also direct object - the constituent of a sentence generally associated with the entity which undergoes the action. In English, the direct object of a verb is a NP and normally follows the verb, e.g. *Peter saw* **Mary**.

OCR Optical Character Reader. A device which scans printed textual material and converts it into electronic form, storing it in a file on the computer or disc. OCR technology has improved dramatically in recent years and is now a reasonably accurate way of making text available in electronic form.

participle the term covers both a word derived from a **verb** and used as an **adjective**, as in *a* **singing** *woman*, and the -ing and -en non-finite forms of the verb, as in *was* **singing** (present participle), *has* **given** (past participle).

particle an element which occurs in a single form (like a preposition in English) and with a function that does not easily fit into standard parts of speech classifications. Particles very often occur in constructions with certain verbs in English with varying degrees of idiosyncratic interpretation: *John took* **off** *at great speed (i.e. left). May gave herself* **up** *(i.e. surrendered)*

part of speech (category) the class of units used in the description of a language, e.g. **noun, verb, noun phrase, verb phrase**.

phonology the branch of linguistics which studies the sound systems of languages. Phonological rules describe the patterns of sounds used distinctively in a language, and phonologists are interested in the question of what constitutes a possible sound system for a natural language.

post-editing program that performs some operations on the output of another program, typically formatting the output for some device or filtering out unwanted items.

predicate traditional and modern grammars often divide sentences so that constituents other than the **subject** are considered together to form the predicate (e.g.

*John (*subject*) kicked the ball (*predicate*))*.

prepositional phrase (PP) a phrase headed by a preposition, a word such as *on, in, between*. Prepositions combine with other constituents (usually noun phrases) to form **prepositional phrases**, as in *The man sat* **on the bench**.

probabilistic a term for approaches to natural language processing (including MT) which rely to some extent on statistical methods.

pronoun a word that can substitute for a **noun phrase** (e.g. *he* can substitute for *John*).

prosodic indicating stress or intonation.

reading a sense of a word that can be distinguished from other senses or meanings of the same word.

relative clause a clause which qualifies or restricts the meaning of the noun in a **noun phrase**. It may be introduced by words such as *who, which* and *that* in English: *the man* **who I saw this morning,** *the woman* **(that) I sent the letter to.**

root that part of a word that is left when all **affixes** have been removed (*industry* is the root of *preindustrial*).

selectional restrictions selectional restrictions are essentially semantic restrictions on combinations of words. For example, verbs place such restrictions on their subjects and objects - the verb *frighten* generally requires as (active) subject something animate which can experience fear.

semantics the branch of linguistics which studies meaning in language. One can distinguish between the study of the meanings of words (lexical semantics) and the study of how the meanings of larger constituents come about (structural semantics).

semantic role also called **deep case, semantic relation** or **thematic role**. A semantic role is a description of the relationship that a constituent plays with respect to the verb in the sentence. The subject of an active sentence is often the **agent** or **experiencer**. Other roles include **instrumental, benefactive, patient:** *Peter* **(experiencer)** *died. The cat* **(agent)** *chased the dog* **(patient)**.

SGML Standard Generalized Markup Language. A generic language for marking various formatting and other textual relationships in a text.

source language when translating, the language one is translating out of; in French to English translation, French is the source language.

speech act a declarative sentence can be used to perform a number of different **speech acts**. In uttering *It's cold in here* a speaker may perform an act of requesting the hearer to close the window or turn up the heating.

stem that part of a word to which **inflectional affixes** are attached (it consists of the **root** plus any **derivational affixes**.

subcategorization the pattern of complements selected by head, e.g. the verb *put* subcategorizes for an NP and a PP. *We put the car in the garage*, but not **We put the car.*

subject the constituent of an active sentence most typically associated with the 'doer' or 'undergoer' of an action. The verb agrees with the subject in person and number in English.

sublanguage a language used to communicate in a specialized technical domain or for a specialized purpose, for example, the language of weather reports, expert scientific polemic or other modes of scientific discourse, user or maintenance manuals, drug interaction reports, etc. Such language is characterised by the high frequency of specialized terminology and often also by a restricted set of grammatical patterns. The interest is that these properties make sublanguage texts easier to translate automatically.

suffix an **affix** that is added following a **root** or **stem**, for example the boldface parts of *legalize, national*.

syntax the rules of a **grammar** which govern the way words are combined to form sentences and other phrases in a language.

tag to tag a text is to annotate it with grammatical information. Usually tagging takes the form of **part-of-speech** annotations but semantic tags or tags encoding other linguistic information can be used. Tagging is usually performed automatically or semi-automatically.

target language when translating, the language one is translating into; in French to English translation, English is the target language.

tense a property of verbs relating primarily to the time at which the action or event denoted by the verb takes place. For example, past tense verbs, as in *Sam left*, describe events in the past.

testsuite a collection of **sentences** or sentence fragments collated to test the capabilities of a translation system or other NLP application.

thesaurus a list of words arranged according to meaning, rather than alphabetically as in a standard dictionary.

transfer the phase in MT where a source language representation is mapped onto a target language representation, a linguistic knowledge based approach to MT where translation proceeds in three stages — analysis (where input string is mapped onto a source language representation) transfer and generation.

Bibliography

[ACL28, 1990] *28th Annual Meeting of the Association for Computational Linguistics*, Pittsburg, Pa., 1990.

[ACL29, 1991] *29th Annual Meeting of the Association for Computational Linguistics*, Berkeley, Ca., 1991.

[ACL30, 1992] *30th Annual Meeting of the Association for Computational Linguistics*, University of Delaware, Newark, Delaware, 1992.

[AECMA, 1988] *AECMA/AIA Simplified English*. AECMA, Paris, 1988.

[Aijmer and Altenberg, 1991] Karin Aijmer and Bengt Altenberg, editors. *English Corpus Linguistics*. Longman, London, 1991.

[Albisser, in press] D. Albisser. Evaluation of MT systems at Union Bank of Switzerland. *Machine Translation*, 7, in press. Special Issue on Evaluation.

[Allegranza *et al.*, 1991] V. Allegranza, P. Bennett, J. Durand, F. Van Eynde, L. Humphreys, P. Schmidt, and E. Steiner. Linguistics for Machine Translation: The Eurotra linguistic specifications. In C. Copeland, J. Durand, S. Krauwer, and B. Maegaard, editors, *The Eurotra Linguistic Specifications*, pages 15–124. CEC, Luxembourg, 1991.

[Allen, 1987] J. Allen. *Natural Language Understanding*. Benjamin Cummings Pub. Co., Inc., Menlo Park, Ca., 1987.

[Allerton, 1984] D.J. Allerton. Three (or four) levels of word cooccurrence restriction. *Lingua*, 63:17–40, 1984.

[Apresian *et al.*, 1992] Jurij Apresian, Igor Boguslavskij, Leonid Iomdin, Alexandre Lazurskij, Vladimir Sannikov, and Leonid Tsinman. ETAP-2: The linguistics of a Machine Translation system. *META*, XXXVII(4):97–112, 1992.

[Arnold and des Tombe, 1987] D.J. Arnold and Louis des Tombe. Basic theory and methodology in Eurotra. In Sergei Nirenburg, editor, *Machine Translation: Theoretical and Methodological Issues*, pages 114–135. Cambridge University Press, Cambridge, 1987.

[Arnold and Sadler, 1989] D.J. Arnold and L.G. Sadler. Non-compositionality and translation. In Jeremy Peckham, editor, *Recent Developments and Applications of Natural Language Processing*, pages 23–55. Kogan Page, London, 1989.

[Arnold and Sadler, 1990] D.J. Arnold and L.G. Sadler. The theoretical basis of MiMo. *Machine Translation*, 5:195–222, 1990.

[Arnold et al., 1988] D.J. Arnold, S. Krauwer, L. des Tombe, and L.G. Sadler. Relaxed compositionality in MT. *Proceedings of the Second International Conference on Theoretical and Methodological Issues in Machine Translation*, 1988.

[Arnold et al., in press a] D.J. Arnold, D. Moffat, L.G. Sadler, and A. Way. Automatic test suite generation. *Machine Translation*, 7, in press . Special Issue on Evaluation.

[Arnold et al., in press b] D.J. Arnold, L.G. Sadler, and R.L. Humphreys. Evaluation: An assessment. *Machine Translation*, 7, in press . Special Issue on Evaluation.

[Arnold, 1986] D.J. Arnold. Eurotra: A European perspective on MT. *Proceedings of the IEEE*, 74(7):979–992, 1986.

[Arnold, 1990] D.J. Arnold. Text typology and Machine Translation: An overview. In Pamela Mayorcas, editor, *Translating and the Computer 10*, pages 73–89. Aslib, London, 1990.

[Arnold, 1993] D.J. Arnold. Sur la conception du transfert. In P. Bouillon and A. Clas, editors, *Etudes et Recherches en Traductique : Problemes de Traduction par Ordinateur*. Presses de Montreal/AUPELF, Montreal, 1993.

[Balkan et al., 1991] L. Balkan, M. Jaeschke, L. Humphreys, S. Meijer, and A. Way. Declarative evaluation of an MT system: Practical experiences. *Applied Computer Translation, 1(3)*, pages 49–59, 1991.

[Bar-Hillel, 1951] Y. Bar-Hillel. The state of translation in 1951. *American Documentation*, 2:229–237, 1951. (Reprinted in Y. Bar-Hillel, *Language and Information*, Addison Wesley, Reading, Mass., 1964, pages 153-165).

[Barr and Fiegenbaum, 1981] Avron Barr and Edward A. Fiegenbaum, editors. *The Handbook of Artificial Intelligence, Vol 1*. William Kaufmann, Inc., Los Altos, California, 1981.

[Bauer, 1983] L. Bauer. *English Word-Formation*. Cambridge University Press, Cambridge, 1983.

[Beaven, 1992] John L. Beaven. Shake-and-bake Machine Translation. *Proceedings of the 15th International Conference on Computational Linguistics, volume II*, pages 602–609, 1992.

[Bennett and Slocum, 1988] W. Scott Bennett and J. Slocum. METAL: the LRC Machine Translation system. In J. Slocum, editor, *Machine Translation Systems*, pages 111–140. CUP, Cambridge, 1988.

[Bennett *et al.*, 1986] P. Bennett, R.L. Johnson, J. McNaught, J.M. Pugh, J.C. Sager, and H.L. Somers, editors. *Multilingual Aspects of Information Technology.* Gower Press, 1986.

[Bennett, 1993] Paul Bennett. The interaction of syntax and morphology in Machine Translation. In F. Van Eynde, editor, *Linguistic Issues in Machine Translation*, pages 72–104. Pinter, London, 1993.

[Benson *et al.*, 1986a] Morton Benson, Evelyn Benson, and Robert Ilson. *The BBI Combinatory Dictionary of English: A Guide to Word Combinations.* John Benjamins Publishing Co., Amsterdam, 1986.

[Benson *et al.*, 1986b] Morton Benson, Evelyn Benson, and Robert Ilson. *Lexicographic Description of English.* Studies in Language Companion Series. John Benjamins Publishing Co., Amsterdam, 1986.

[Berlin and Kay, 1969] B. Berlin and P. Kay. *Basic Color Terms: Their Universality and Evolution.* University of California Press, Berkeley, Ca., 1969.

[Boguraev and Briscoe, 1989] B. Boguraev and E. Briscoe, editors. *Computational Lexicography for Natural Language Processing.* Longman, London, 1989.

[Borsley, 1991] Robert D. Borsley. *Syntactic Theory: A Unified Approach.* Edward Arnold, London, 1991.

[Bratko, 1986] I. Bratko. *Prolog Programming for Artificial Intelligence.* Addison Wesley, Wokingham, 1986.

[Brown and Miller, 1991] E.K. Brown and J.E. Miller. *Syntax: A Linguistic Introduction to Sentence Structure.* Harper Collins, London, 1991.

[Brown *et al.*, 1990] P.F. Brown, J. Cocke, S.A. Della Pietra, F. Jelinek, J.D. Lafferty, R.L. Mercer, and P.S. Roossin. A statistical approach to Machine Translation. *Computational Linguistics*, 16:79–85, 1990.

[Brown *et al.*, 1991] P.F. Brown, J.C. Lai, and R.L. Mercer. Aligning sentences in parallel corpora. In *Proceedings of 29th ACL*, pages 169–176, Berkeley, California, 1991.

[Bruce, 1972] Bertram Bruce. A model for temporal reference and its application in a question answering program. *Artificial Intelligence*, 3:1–25, 1972.

[Buchmann, 1987] B. Buchmann. Early history of Machine Translation. In M. King, editor, *Machine Translation Today: The State of the Art, Proceedings of the Third Lugano Tutorial, 1984*, pages 3–21. Edinburgh University Press, Edinburgh, 1987.

[Cann, 1993] Ronnie Cann. *Formal Semantics.* Cambridge University Press, Cambridge, 1993.

[Chandioux, 1976] J. Chandioux. Météo: Un système opérationnel pour la traduction automatique des bulletins météorologiques destinés au grand public. *META*, 21:127–133, 1976.

[Chandioux, 1989a] J. Chandioux. 10 ans de Météo (MD). In A. Abbou, editor, *Traduction Assistée par Ordinateur: Perspectives Technologiques, Industrielles et Économiques Envisageables à l'Horizon 1990: l'Offre, la Demande, les Marchés et les Évolutions en Cours*, pages 169–172. Editions Daicadif, Paris, 1989.

[Chandioux, 1989b] J. Chandioux. Météo: 100 million words later. In D.L. Hammond, editor, *American Translators Association Conference 1989: Coming of Age*, pages 449–453. Learned Information, Medford, NJ, 1989.

[Charniak and McDermott, 1985] Eugene Charniak and Drew McDermott. *An Introduction to Artificial Intelligence*. Addison Wesley, Reading, Mass, 1985.

[Charniak and Wilks, 1976] E. Charniak and Y. Wilks, editors. *Computational Semantics*. North Holland Pub. Co.,, Amsterdam, 1976.

[Chierchia and McConnell-Ginet, 1990] G. Chierchia and S. McConnell-Ginet. *Meaning and Grammar: An Introduction to Semantics*. MIT Press, Cambridge, Mass., 1990.

[Coling84, 1984] *Proceedings of the Eleventh International Conference on Computational Linguistics*, Stanford University, California, 1984.

[Coling86, 1986] *Proceedings of the Twelfth International Conference on Computational Linguistics*, University of Bonn, 1986.

[Coling88, 1988] Coling88. *Proceedings of the Thirteenth International Conference on Computational Linguistics*, volume 1-2, Budapest, 1988. John von Neumann Society for Computing Sciences.

[Coling90, 1990] *Proceedings of the Fourteenth International Conference on Computational Linguistics*, volume 1-3, Helsinki University, 1990.

[Coling92, 1992] *Proceedings of the Fifteenth International Conference on Computational Linguistics*, volume 1-4, Université de Nantes, 1992.

[Copeland *et al.*, 1991a] C. Copeland, J. Durand, S. Krauwer, and B. Maegaard, editors. *The Eurotra Formal Specifications*, volume 2 of *Studies in Machine Translation and Natural Language Processing*. Office for Official Publications of the Commission of the European Community, Luxembourg, 1991.

[Copeland *et al.*, 1991b] C. Copeland, J. Durand, S. Krauwer, and B. Maegaard, editors. *The Eurotra Linguistic Specifications*, volume 1 of *Studies in Machine Translation and Natural Language Processing*. Office for Official Publications of the Commission of the European Community, Luxembourg, 1991.

[Danlos and Samvelian, 1992] L. Danlos and P. Samvelian. Translation of the predicative element of a sentence: Category switching, aspect and diathesis. *Fourth International Conference on Theoretical and Methodological Issues in Machine Translation*, pages 21–34, 1992.

[Danlos, 1992] L. Danlos. Support verb constructions: Linguistic properties, representation, translation. *Journal of French Language Studies*, 2(1), 1992.

[Dyvik, 1992] Helge Dyvik. The PONS system: Translation by principled rules of thumb (partial translation between closely related languages). Unpublished Ms., Dept. of Linguistics and Phonetics, University of Bergen, 1992.

[EACL1, 1983] *Proceedings of the First Conference of the European Chapter of the Association for Computational Linguistics*, Pisa, Italy, 1983.

[EACL2, 1985] *Proceedings of the Second Conference of the European Chapter of the Association for Computational Linguistics*, University of Geneva, Switzerland, 1985.

[EACL3, 1987] *Proceedings of the Third Conference of the European Chapter of the Association for Computational Linguistics*, University of Copenhagen, Denmark, 1987.

[EACL4, 1989] *Proceedings of the Fourth Conference of the European Chapter of the Association for Computational Linguistics*, UMIST, UK, 1989.

[EACL5, 1991] *Proceedings of the Fifth Conference of the European Chapter of the Association for Computational Linguistics*, Berlin, 1991.

[Estival et al., 1990] Dominique Estival, Afzal Ballim, Graham Russell, and Susan Warwick. A syntax and semantics for feature-structure transfer. In *Proceedings of the 3rd International Conference on Theoretical and Methodological Issues in Machine Translation of Natural Language*, pages 131–143, Linguistics Research Centre, University of Texas at Austin, USA, 1990.

[Evens, 1988] M.W. Evens, editor. *Relational Models of the Lexicon: Representing Knowledge in Semantic Networks*. Cambridge University Press, Cambridge, 1988.

[Flank et al., in press] S. Flank, A. Temin, H. Blejer, A. Kehler, and S. Greenstein. Module-level testing for natural language understanding. *Machine Translation*, 7, in press. Special Issue on Evaluation.

[Furuse and Iida, 1992a] Osamu Furuse and Hitoshi Iida. Cooperation between transfer and analysis in example-based framework. In *Proceedings of the 15th International Conference on Computational Linguistics, volume II*, pages 645–651, Nantes, France, 1992.

[Furuse and Iida, 1992b] Osamu Furuse and Hitoshi Iida. An example-based method for transfer-driven Machine Translation. In *Fourth International Conference on Theoretical and Methodological Issues in Machine Translation*, pages 139–150, Montreal, Canada, 1992.

[Gale and Church, 1991a] W.A. Gale and K.W. Church. Identifying word correspondence and parallel text. In *4th DARPA Workshop on Speech and Natural Language*, Asilomar, 1991.

[Gale and Church, 1991b] W.A. Gale and K.W. Church. A program for aligning sentences in bilingual corpora. In *Proceedings of the 29th ACL*, pages 177–184, University of California, Berkeley, Ca., 1991.

[Garside *et al.*, 1987] Roger Garside, Geoffrey Leech, and Geoffrey Sampson, editors. *The Computational Analysis of English: A Corpus-Based Approach*. Longman, London, 1987.

[Gazdar and Mellish, 1989] G. Gazdar and C. Mellish. *Natural Language Processing in Prolog*. Addison Wesley, Wokingham, 1989.

[Goldfarb, 1986] C.F. Goldfarb, editor. *The Standard Generalized Markup Language (ISO 8879)*. International Organisation for Standardization, Geneva, 1986.

[Goodman and Nirenburg, 1991] Kenneth Goodman and Sergei Nirenburg, editors. *The KBMT Project: A Case Study in Knowledge Based Machine Translation*. Morgan Kaufmann, San Mateo, California, 1991.

[Goodman, 1989] K. Goodman, editor. *Machine Translation*, volume 4. 1989. numbers 1 and 2 : Special Issues on Knowledge Based MT, Parts I and II.

[Grimaila and Chandioux, 1992] Annette Grimaila and John Chandioux. Made to measure solutions. In John Newton, editor, *Computers in Translation: A Practical Appraisal*, pages 33–45. Routledge, London, 1992.

[Grishman and Kittredge, 1986] R. Grishman and R.I. Kittredge, editors. *Analyzing Language in Restricted Domains: Sublanguage Description and Processing*. Lawrence Erlbaum Associates, New Jersey: Hillsdale, 1986.

[Grishman, 1986] Ralph Grishman. *Computational Linguistics: An Introduction*. Cambridge University Press, Cambridge, 1986.

[Grosz and Sidner, 1986] B.J. Grosz and C.L. Sidner. Attention, intentions, and the structure of discourse. *Computational Linguistics*, 12:175–204, 1986.

[Guida and Mauri, July 1986] Giovanni Guida and Giancarlo Mauri. Evaluation of Natural Language processing systems: Issues and approaches. *Proceedings of the IEEE*, 74(7):1026–1035, July 1986.

[Hanks and Church, 1989] Patrick Hanks and Kenneth W. Church. Word association norms, mutual information and lexicography. *27th Annual Meeting of the Association for Comutational Linguistics*, pages 22–29, 1989.

[Hatim and Mason, 1990] Basil Hatim and Ian Mason. *Discourse and the Translator*. Longman, London, 1990.

[Hirschman, 1986] L. Hirschman. Discovering sublanguage structures. In R. Grishman and R.I. Kittredge, editors, *Analyzing Language in Restricted Domains: Sublanguage Description and Processing*, pages 211–234. Lawrence Erlbaum Associates, New Jersey: Hillsdale, 1986.

[Hornby *et al.*, 1974] A.S. Hornby, A.P. Cowie, and A.C. Gimson. *Oxford Advanced Learner's Dictionary of Current English*. Oxford University Press, Oxford, 1974.

[Hurford and Heasley, 1983] J.R. Hurford and B. Heasley. *Semantics: A Course Book*. Cambridge University Press, Cambridge, 1983.

[Hutchins and Somers, 1992] W.J. Hutchins and H.L. Somers. *An Introduction to Machine Translation*. Academic Press, London, 1992.

[Hutchins, 1986] W.J. Hutchins. *Machine Translation: Past, Present, Future*. Ellis Horwood/Wiley, Chichester/New York, 1986.

[Isabelle, 1987] P. Isabelle. Machine Translation at the TAUM group. In M. King, editor, *Machine Translation Today: The State of the Art, Proceedings of the Third Lugano Tutorial, 1984*, pages 247–277. Edinburgh University Press, Edinburgh, 1987.

[Jordan, in press] P.W. Jordan. A first-pass approach for evaluating Machine Translation systems. *Machine Translation*, 7, in press. Special Issue on Evaluation.

[Kaplan *et al.*, 1989] Ronald M. Kaplan, Klaus Netter, Jurgen Wedekind, and Annie Zaenen. Translation by structural correspondences. In *Proceedings of the Fourth Conference of the European Chapter of the Association for Computational Linguistics*, pages 272–281, University of Manchester, Institute of Science and Technology, Manchester, UK, 1989.

[Katz, 1978] J.J. Katz. Effability and translation. In F. Guenthner and M. Guenthner-Reutter, editors, *Meaning and Translation*, pages 191–234. Duckworth, London, 1978.

[Keenan, 1978] E.L. Keenan. Some logical problems in translation. In F. Guenthner and M. Guenthner-Reutter, editors, *Meaning and Translation*, pages 157–190. Duckworth, London, 1978.

[Kempson, 1977] Ruth Kempson. *Semantic Theory*. Cambridge University Press, Cambridge, 1977.

[King and Falkedal, 1990] M. King and K. Falkedal. Using test suites in evaluation of MT systems. In *COLING-90*, volume 2, pages 211–216, Helsinki, Finland, 1990.

[King, 1987] Margaret King, editor. *Machine Translation Today: The State of the Art*. Edinburgh University Press, Edinburgh, 1987.

[Kittredge, 1982] R.I. Kittredge. Variation and homogeneity of sublanguages. In R.I. Kittredge and J. Lehrberger, editors, *Sublanguage*, pages 107–137. Walter de Gruyter, Berlin, 1982.

[Kittredge, 1987] R.I. Kittredge. The significance of sublanguage for Automatic Translation. In S. Nirenburg, editor, *Machine Translation Systems*, pages 59–67. Cambridge University Press, Cambridge, 1987.

[Knowles, 1990] Francis E. Knowles. Machine aids for translators: what does the future betoken? In Pamela Mayorcas, editor, *Translating and the Computer 10*, pages 125–135. Aslib, London, 1990.

[Krauwer, in press] Steven Krauwer. Evaluation of MT systems: A programmatic view. *Machine Translation*, 7, in press. Special Issue on Evaluation.

[Landsbergen, 1987a] Jan S.P. Landsbergen. Isomorphic grammars and their use in the Rosetta translation system. In Margaret King, editor, *Machine Translation Today: The State of the Art, Proceedings of the Third Lugano Tutorial, 1984*, pages 351–372. Edinburgh University Press, Edinburgh, 1987.

[Landsbergen, 1987b] Jan S.P. Landsbergen. Montague grammar and Machine Translation. In Peter Whitelock, Mary McGee Wood, Harold L. Somers, Rod L. Johnson, and Paul Bennett, editors, *Linguistic Theory and Computer Applications*, pages 113–147. Academic Press, London, 1987.

[Lawson, 1982a] Veronica Lawson, editor. *Practical Experience of Machine Translation*. North-Holland, Amsterdam, 1982.

[Lawson, 1982b] Veronica Lawson, editor. *Translating and the Computer 5: Tools for the Trade*. North-Holland, Amsterdam, 1982.

[Leech, 1983] Geoffrey N. Leech. *Principles of Pragmatics*. Longman Linguistics Library. Longman, 1983.

[Lehrberger and Bourbeau, 1987] John Lehrberger and Laurent Bourbeau. *Machine Translation: Linguistic Characteristics of MT Systems and General Methodology of Evaluation*. John Benjamins, Amsterdam, 1987.

[Lehrberger, 1982] J. Lehrberger. Automatic translation and the concept of sublanguage. In R.I. Kittredge and J. Lehrberger, editors, *Sublanguage*, pages 81–107. Walter de Gruyter, Berlin, 1982.

[Levinson, 1983] Stephen C. Levinson. *Pragmatics*. Cambridge Textbooks in Linguistics. Cambridge University Press, Cambridge, 1983.

[Maas, 1987] Heinz-Dieter Maas. The MT system SUSY. In Margaret King, editor, *Machine Translation Today: The State of the Art, Proceedings of the Third Lugano Tutorial, 1984*, pages 209–246. Edinburgh University Press, Edinburgh, 1987.

[Mayorcas, 1990] Pamela Mayorcas, editor. *Translating and the Computer 10: The Translation Environment 10 Years on*. Aslib, London, 1990.

[Mayorcas, Forthcoming] Pamela Mayorcas, editor. *Translating and the Computer 12*. Aslib, London, Forthcoming.

[McCord, 1989] Michael C. McCord. Design of LMT: A Prolog-based Machine Translation system. *Computational Linguistics*, 15(1):33–52, 1989.

[McDonald, 1987] David D. McDonald. Natural Language generation: Complexities and techniques. In Sergei Nirenberg, editor, *Machine Translation: Theoretical and Methodological Issues*, pages 192–224. Cambridge University Press, Cambridge, 1987.

[McNaught, 1988a] J. McNaught. Computational Lexicography and Computational Linguistics. *Lexicographica (Special Issue on Computational Lexicography)*, 4:19–33, 1988.

[McNaught, 1988b] J. McNaught. A survey of term banks worldwide. In C. Picken, editor, *Translating and the Computer*, pages 112–129. Aslib, London, 1988.

[McNaught, forthcoming] J. McNaught. Toward the neutral lexical database. In D. Walker, A. Zampolli, and N. Calzolari, editors, *Towards a Polytheoretical Lexical Database*. Istituto di Linguistica Computazionale, Pisa, forthcoming.

[Melby, 1987] A. Melby. On human machine interaction in Machine Translation. In Sergei Nirenburg, editor, *Machine Translation: Theoretical and Methodological Issues*, pages 145–54. Cambridge University Press, Cambridge, 1987.

[Melby, 1992] A. Melby. The translator workstation. In John Newton, editor, *Computers in Translation: A Practical Appraisal*, pages 147–165. Routledge, London, 1992.

[Mel'čuk and Polguere, 1987] I.A. Mel'čuk and A. Polguere. A formal lexicon in the meaning-text theory. *Computational Linguistics*, 13:261–275, 1987.

[Mel'čuk and Zholkovsky, 1988] Igor Mel'čuk and Alexander Zholkovsky. The explanatory combinatory dictionary. In M.W. Evens, editor, *Relational Models of the Lexicon: Representing Knowledge in Semantic Networks*, pages 41–74. CUP, 1988.

[Minnis, in press] S. Minnis. Constructive Machine Translation evaluation. *Machine Translation*, 7, in press. Special Issue on Evaluation.

[Nagao et al., July 1986] Makoto Nagao, Jun-ichi Tsujii, and Jun-ichi Nakamura. Machine Translation from Japanese into English. *Proceedings of the IEEE*, 74(7):993–1012, July 1986.

[Nagao, 1984] M. Nagao. A framework of a mechanical translation between Japanese and English by analogy principle. In A. Elithorn and R. Banerji, editors, *Artificial and Human Intelligence*, pages 173–180. North Holland, Amsterdam, 1984.

[Nagao, 1986] Makoto Nagao. *Machine Translation: How Far Can it Go?* Oxford University Press, Oxford, 1986. Translated by Norman Cook.

[Nagao, 1989] M. Nagao, editor. *Machine Translation Summit*. Ohmsha Ltd, Tokyo Japan, 1989.

[Neal et al., in press] J.G. Neal, E.L. Feit, and A. Montgomery. Benchmark investigation/identification project, phase 1. *Machine Translation*, 7, in press. Special Issue on Evaluation.

[Nerbonne et al., in press] J. Nerbonne, K. Netter, A.K. Diagne, J. Klein, and L. Dickmann. A diagnostic tool for German syntax. *Machine Translation*, 7, in press. Special Issue on Evaluation.

[Newton, 1992a] John Newton, editor. *Computers in Translation: A Practical Appraisal*. Routledge, London, 1992.

[Newton, 1992b] John Newton. The Perkins experience. In John Newton, editor, *Computers in Translation: A Practical Appraisal*, pages 46–57. Routledge, London, 1992.

[Nirenburg, 1993] S. Nirenburg. Interlangue et traitement du sens dans les systèmes de TA. In P.Bouillon and A.Clas, editors, *Etudes et Recherches en Traductique : Problemes de Traduction par Ordinateur*. Presses de Montreal/AUPELF, Montreal, 1993.

[Paillet, 1990] Alain Paillet. User experience of Termbase. In Pamela Mayorcas, editor, *Translating and the Computer 10*, pages 97–108. Aslib, London, 1990.

[Patterson, 1982] B. Patterson. Multilingualism in the European Community. *Multilingua*, 1(1):4–15, 1982.

[Picken, 1985] C. Picken, editor. *Translating and the Computer 6: Translation and Communication*. Aslib, London, 1985.

[Picken, 1986] C. Picken, editor. *Translating and the Computer 7*. Aslib, London, 1986.

[Picken, 1987] C. Picken, editor. *Translating and the Computer 8: A Profession on the Move*. Aslib, London, 1987.

[Picken, 1988] C. Picken, editor. *Translating and the Computer 9: Potential and Practice*. Aslib, London, 1988.

[Picken, 1989] C. Picken, editor. *The Translator's Handbook*. Aslib, London, 2nd edition, 1989.

[Picken, 1990] C. Picken, editor. *Translating and the Computer 11: Preparing for the Next Decade*. Aslib, London, 1990.

[Pierce and Carroll, 1966] John R. Pierce and John B. Carroll. *Language and Machines - Computers in Translation and Linguistics (ALPAC Report)*. ALPAC, Washington D.C., 1966.

[Pollard and Sag, 1987] Carl Pollard and Ivan Sag. *Information Based Syntax and Semantics*, volume 1: Fundamentals of *CSLI Lecture Notes, 13*. Chicago University Press, Chicago, 1987.

[Pollard and Sag, 1993] Carl Pollard and Ivan Sag. *An Information Based Approach to Syntax and Semantics: Vol 2: Agreement, Binding and Control.* Chicago University Press, Chicago, 1993.

[Proctor, 1978] P. Proctor, editor. *Longman's Dictionary of Contemporary English.* Longman Group Ltd., Harlow, UK, 1978.

[Pugh, 1992] Jeanette Pugh. The story so far: An evaluation of Machine Translation in the world today. In John Newton, editor, *Computers in Translation: A Practical Appraisal*, pages 14–32. Routledge, London, 1992.

[Pullum, 1991] Geoffrey K. Pullum. *The Great Eskimo Vocabulary Hoax.* Chicago University Press, Chicago, 1991.

[Pustejovsky and Bergler, 1992] J. Pustejovsky and S. Bergler, editors. *Lexical Semantics and Knowledge Representation.* Springer-Verlag, Berlin, 1992.

[Pustejovsky, 1987] J. Pustejovsky. An integrated theory of discourse analysis. In Sergei Nirenburg, editor, *Machine Translation: Theoretical and Methodological Issues*, pages 169–191. Cambridge University Press, Cambridge, 1987.

[Pym, 1990] D.J. Pym. Pre-editing and the use of simplified writing for MT: An engineer's experience of operating an MT system. In Pamela Mayorcas, editor, *Translating and the Computer 10*, pages 80–96. Aslib, London, 1990.

[Reichenbach, 1947] Hans Reichenbach. *Elements of Symbolic Logic.* University of California Press, Berkeley, Ca., 1947.

[Rich, 1983] Elaine Rich. *Artificial Intelligence.* McGraw-Hill Book Co., Singapore, 1983.

[Ritchie et al., 1992] G.D. Ritchie, G.J. Russell, A.W. Black, and S.G. Pulman. *Computational Morphology: Practical Mechanisms for the English Lexicon.* MIT Press, Cambridge, Mass., 1992.

[Ritchie, 1987] G.D. Ritchie. The lexicon. In Peter Whitelock, Mary McGee Wood, Harold L. Somers, Rod L. Johnson, and Paul Bennett, editors, *Linguistic Theory and Computer Applications*, pages 225–256. Academic Press, London, 1987.

[Rogers, 1986] J.B. Rogers. *A Prolog Primer.* Addison Wesley, Wokingham, 1986.

[Sadler and Arnold, 1993] Louisa Sadler and D.J. Arnold. Unification and Machine Translation. *META*, 37(4):657–680, 1993.

[Sadler, 1989] V. Sadler. *Working with Analogical Semantics: Disambiguation Techniques in DLT.* Distributed Language Translation, 5. Foris Pub., Dordrecht, 1989.

[Sadler, 1991] Louisa Sadler. Structural transfer and unification formalisms. *Applied Computer Translation*, 1(4):5–21, 1991.

[Sadler, 1993] Louisa Sadler. Co-description and translation. In F. Van Eynde, editor, *Linguistic Issues in Machine Translation*, pages 44–71. Pinter, London, 1993.

[Sager, 1982] J.C. Sager. Types of translation and text forms in the environment of Machine Translation (MT). In V. Lawson, editor, *Practical Experience of Machine Translation*, pages 11–19. North Holland Publishing Co, Dordrecht, 1982.

[Sager, 1990] J.C. Sager. *A Practical Course in Terminology Processing*. John Benjamins, 1990.

[Schenk, 1986] A. Schenk. Idioms in the Rosetta Machine Translation system. *Proceedings of COLING 86*, pages 319–324, 1986.

[Schubert, 1992] Klaus Schubert. Esperanto as an intermediate language for Machine Translation. In John Newton, editor, *Computers in Translation: A Practical Appraisal*, pages 78–95. Routledge, London, 1992.

[Shapiro, 1987] S.C. Shapiro, editor. *Encyclopaedia of AI*. Wiley, New York, 1987.

[Sharp, 1988] Randall Sharp. CAT-2 – implementing a formalism for multi-lingual MT. In *Proceedings of the 2nd International Conference on Theoretical and Methodological Issues in Machine Translation of Natural Languages*, pages 76–87, Carnegie Mellon University, Centre for Machine Translation, Pittsburgh, USA, 1988.

[Shiwen, in press] Yu Shiwen. Automatic evaluation of output quality for machine translation systems. *Machine Translation*, 7, in press. Special Issue on Evaluation.

[Sinclair, 1987] J. M. Sinclair, editor. *Looking Up: An Account of the COBUILD Project in Lexical Computing*. Collins ELT, London, 1987.

[Slocum et al., 1987] J. Slocum, W.S. Bennett, J. Bear, M. Morgan, and R. Root. Metal: The LRC Machine Translation system. In M. King, editor, *Machine Translation Today*, pages 319–350. Edinburgh University Press, Edinburgh, 1987.

[Slocum, 1986] J. Slocum. How one might identify and adapt to a sublanguage: An initial exploration. In R. Grishman and R.I. Kittredge, editors, *Analyzing Language in Restricted Domains: Sublanguage Description and Processing*, pages 195–210. Lawrence Erlbaum Associates, New Jersey: Hillsdale, 1986.

[Slocum, 1988] J. Slocum, editor. *Machine Translation Systems*. Cambridge University Press, Cambridge, 1988.

[Snell, 1979] Barbara Snell, editor. *Machine Aids for Translators: Translating and the Computer 2*. North Holland, Amsterdam, 1979.

[Snell, 1982] Barbara Snell, editor. *Term Banks for Tomorrow's World: Translating and the Computer 4*. Aslib, London, 1982.

[Somers, 1992] Harold L. Somers. Current research in Machine Translation. In John Newton, editor, *Computers in Translation: A Practical Appraisal*, pages 189–207. Routledge, London, 1992.

[Sowa, 1984] John F. Sowa. *Conceptual Structures: Information Processing in Mind and Machine*. Addison Wesley, Reading, Mass., 1984.

[Spencer, 1991] A. Spencer. *Morphological Theory*. Basil Blackwell, Oxford, 1991.

[Stoll, 1988] C.H. Stoll. Translation tools on PC. In C. Picken, editor, *Translating and the Computer 9: Potential and Practice*, pages 11–26. Aslib, 1988.

[Sumita and Iida, 1991] E. Sumita and H. Iida. Experiments and prospects of example-based Machine Translation. In *Proceedings of 29th ACL*, pages 185–192, University of California, Berkeley, Ca., 1991.

[Sumita et al., 1990] Eiichiro Sumita, Hitoshi Iida, and Hideo Kohyama. Translating with examples: A new approach to Machine Translation. In *Proceedings of the 3rd International Conference on Theoretical and Methodological Issues in Machine Translation of Natural Language*, pages 203–212, Linguistics Research Centre, University of Texas at Austin, USA, 1990.

[Teller et al., 1988] V. Teller, M. Kosaka, and R. Grishman. A comparative study of Japanese and English sublanguage patterns. In S. Nirenburg, editor, *Proceedings of the Second Conference on Theoretical and Methodological Issues in MT*, Pittsburg, Pa, 1988. Carnegie Mellon University.

[Tennant, 1981] H. Tennant. *Natural Language Processing: An Introduction to an Emerging Technology*. Petrocelli Pub., New York, 1981.

[Thomas, 1992] Patricia Thomas. Computerized term banks and translation. In John Newton, editor, *Computers in Translation: A Practical Appraisal*, pages 131–146. Routledge, London, 1992.

[TMI1, 1985] *Proceedings of the Conference on Theoretical and Methodological Issues in Machine Translation of Natural Languages*, Colgate University, Hamilton, New York, 1985.

[TMI2, 1988] *Second International Conference on Theoretical and Methodological Issues in Machine Translation of Natural Languages*, Carnegie Mellon University, Pittsburgh, 1988.

[TMI3, 1990] *Third International Conference on Theoretical and Methodological Issues in Machine Translation of Natural Language*, University of Texas, Austin, 1990.

[TMI4, 1992] *Fourth International Conference on Theoretical and Methodological Issues in Machine Translation*, CCRIT - CWARC, Montré al, Canada, 1992.

[Tsujii et al., 1992] Jun-ichi Tsujii, Sofia Ananiadou, Iris Arad, and Satoshi Sekine. Linguistic knowledge acquisition from corpora. In Sofia Ananiadou, editor, *International Workshop on Fundamental Research for the Future Generation of Natural Language Processing (FGNLP)*, pages 61–81. CEC, UMIST, Manchester, UK, 1992.

[Van Eynde, 1993a] F. Van Eynde. Machine Translation and linguistic motivation. In F. Van Eynde, editor, *Linguistic Issues in Machine Translation*, pages 1–43. Pinter, London, 1993.

[Van Eynde, 1993b] Frank Van Eynde, editor. *Linguistic Issues in Machine Translation*. Pinter, London, 1993.

[van Herwijnen, 1990] Eric van Herwijnen. *Practical SGML*. Kluwer Academic Publishers, Dordrecht, 1990.

[van Noord et al., 1990] G. van Noord, J. Dorrepaal, P. van der Eijk, M. Florenza, and L. des Tombe. The MiMo2 research system. In *Third International Conference on Theoretical and Methodological Issues in Machine Transation 11-13 June 1990*, pages 213–124, Linguistics Research Center, Austin, Texas, 1990.

[van Slype, 1982] G. van Slype. Conception d'une méthodologie générale d'Evaluation de la Traduction Automatique. *Multilingua*, 1(4):221–237, 1982.

[Vasconcellos, 1988] M. Vasconcellos, editor. *Technology as Translation Strategy*. State University of New York, Binghampton, 1988.

[Vauquois and Boitet, 1985] Bernard Vauquois and Christian Boitet. Automated translation at Grenoble University. *Computational Linguistics*, 11(1):28–36, 1985.

[Vinay and Darbelnet, 1977] J.P. Vinay and J. Darbelnet. *Stylistique Comparé du Français et de l'Anglais*. Didier, Paris, 1977.

[Warwick, 1987] Susan Warwick. An overview of post-ALPAC developments. In Margaret King, editor, *Machine Translation Today: The State of the Art, Proceedings of the Third Lugano Tutorial, 1984*, pages 22–37. Edinburgh University Press, Edinburgh, 1987.

[Whitelock, 1992] P. Whitelock. Shake-and-bake translation. *Proceedings of the 15th International Conference on Computational Linguistics (COLING 92), volume II*, pages 784–791, 1992.

[Wilks, 1973] Y.A. Wilks. An Artificial Intelligence approach to Machine Translation. In R.C. Schank and K.M. Colby, editors, *Computer Models of Thought and Language*, pages 114–151. Freeman, San Francisco, 1973.

[Wilks, 1992] Yorick Wilks. Systran: It obviously works but how much can it be improved? In John Newton, editor, *Computers in Translation: A Practical Appraisal*, pages 166–188. Routledge, London, 1992.

[Winograd, 1983] T. Winograd. *Language as a Cognitive Process*. Addison Wesley, Reading, Mass., 1983.

Index